Wonders of Learning

Pre-Kindergarten

WORKBOOK

varuntej

sireesha

Pavankumar

© 2021 North Parade Publishing

By Jennifer G. Bove, Kris Anah Allard, Joel Riemer

Design and illustrations by QBS Learning; additional images by Shutterstock

Published by North Parade Publishing, Bath BA2 6JW, United Kingdom

ISBN 9781839233456

Printed in China, Guangdong Province August 2021

Second Printing

24 23 22 21 2 3 4 5

Contents

Dear Family,

What does it mean when we say that *Wonders of Learning* workbooks have been crafted with your child in mind?

Of course, we have not met your child. But we understand the uniqueness of each child's learning path, as well as the developmental stages that children have in common. We are a small team of instructional designers with many decades of experience teaching and creating curriculum for children of all ages and abilities. Among us are specialists in nurturing both advanced learners and those who face challenges. We are classroom teachers, home-school consultants, children's book writers, and experts in designing meaningful learning experiences that align with Common Core and state-level standards.

Each page is designed to facilitate effective and enjoyable learning, either as a supplement to school-based learning or as part of a home-based course of study. Classic "pencil-and-paper" activities are complemented by pages that provide hands-on and enquiry-based learning opportunities.

Because children learn at different rates, pages are designed so that some children may complete them on their own while others may need more help from you. In the earliest years, your child will need you to read instructions aloud.

You are your child's first teacher and, whether your child attends school or studies at home, you will always be an important teacher. The earliest learning happens naturally and through repetition. Children learn about words and concepts each time you call something by its name—the difference between a cat and a dog, for example. They learn to count each time you use numbers to describe objects or events in everyday life. And many children learn to read by unconsciously memorizing picture books that are read to them frequently.

Have fun working through this book with your child. Encourage curiosity as you explore new concepts and practice familiar ones. And throughout daily life, read to your child as often as possible, name and count what you see, and keep answering children's questions!

We have put our hearts into providing a resource that will be meaningful and memorable for your child, and we hope that you enjoy the results.

Yours Sincerely,

Jennifer

Jennifer Bove, MSEd
lead author, developmental editor

Reading ABCs

USING THIS SECTION

In these pages, children will learn the shapes of letters. This is the "seeing" modality of learning to read. Although pictures are used that begin with each letter, the focus is on saying the letter's name and recognizing the capital and lowercase forms. On many pages, children will color shapes with the targeted letter. After they follow directions, they may want to color the rest of the page. Allow them to do so, because children should have a sense of ownership and enjoyment of this book. However, you might suggest using different colors. For example, if children choose red for apples with the letter A, they might choose green or yellow for the other apples.

A

Read **capital A**.

Color the apples with capital A.

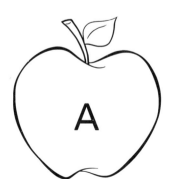

a

Read **lowercase a**.

Color the apples with lowercase a.

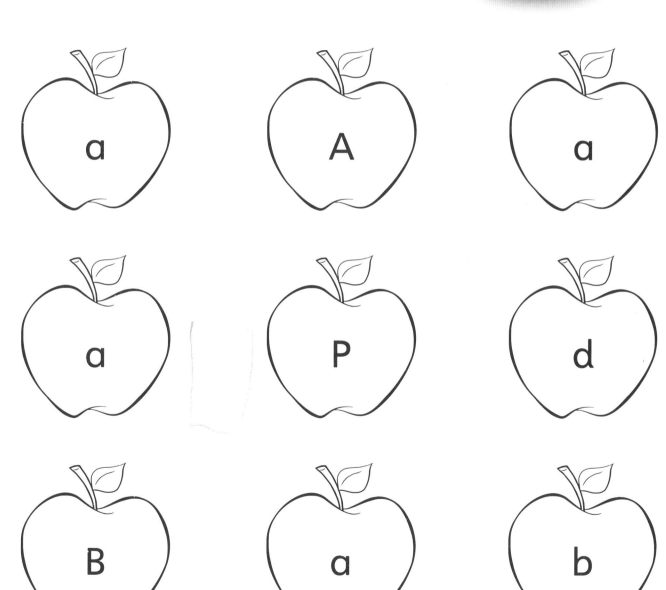

B

Read **capital B**.

Color the stripes with capital B.

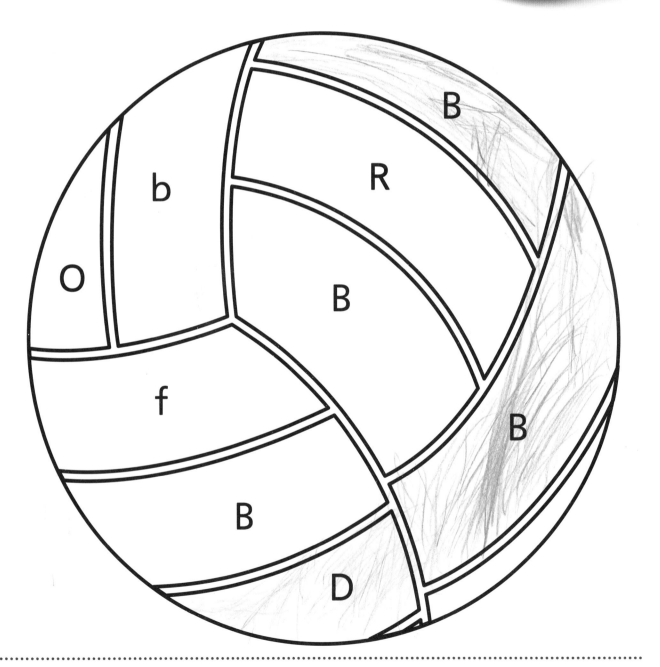

b

Read **lowercase b**.

Color the stripes with lowercase b.

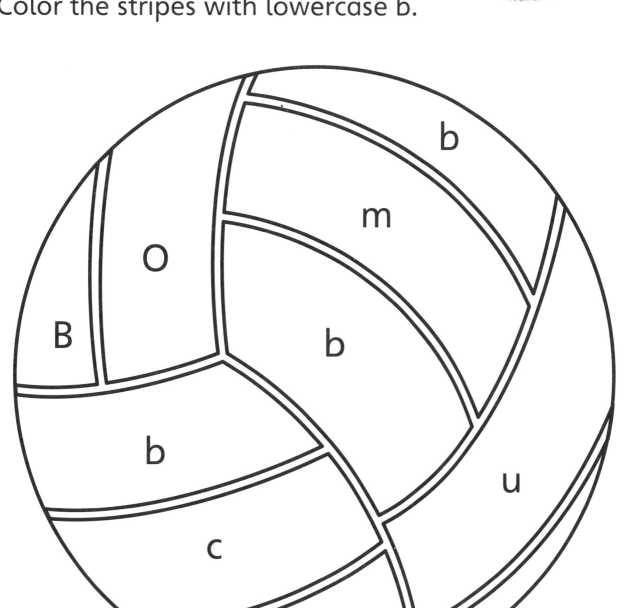

C

Read **capital C**.

Circle each capital C.
Then color the cat.

C

Read **lowercase c**.

Circle each lowercase c.
Then color the cat.

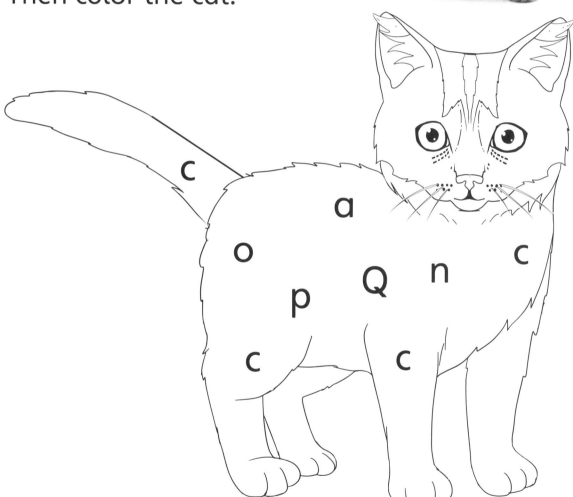

Did you know?
Cats have whiskers on their faces.
Their whiskers help cats find their way
in the dark and in small spaces.

D

Read **capital D**.

Color each circle that has capital D.

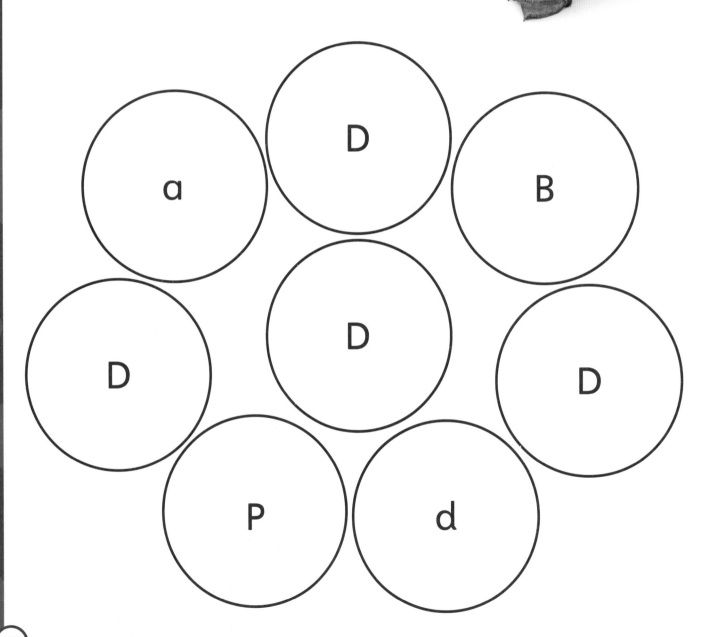

d

Read **lowercase d**.

Color each square that has lowercase d.

D	d

d	p	d
a	d	o

E

Read **capital E**.

Color the eggs with capital E.

E

o

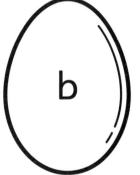
e

H

E

b

E

J

E

e

Read **lowercase e**.

Color the eggs with lowercase e.

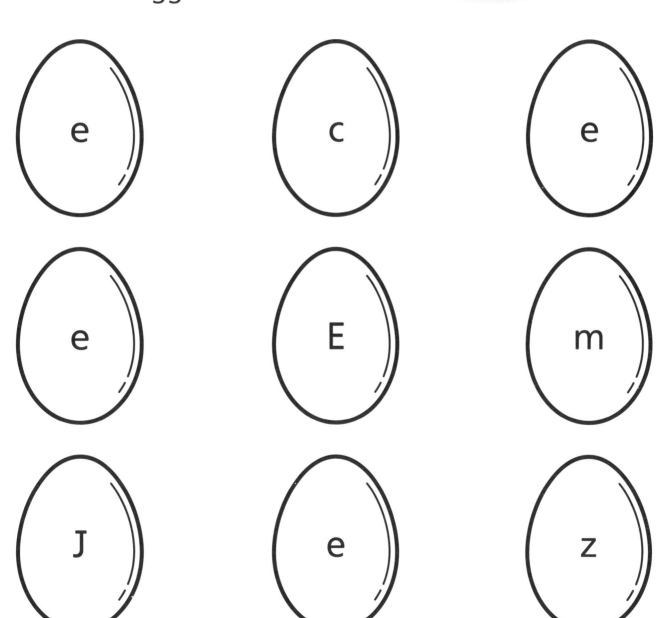

F

Read **capital F**.

Color the bubbles with capital F.

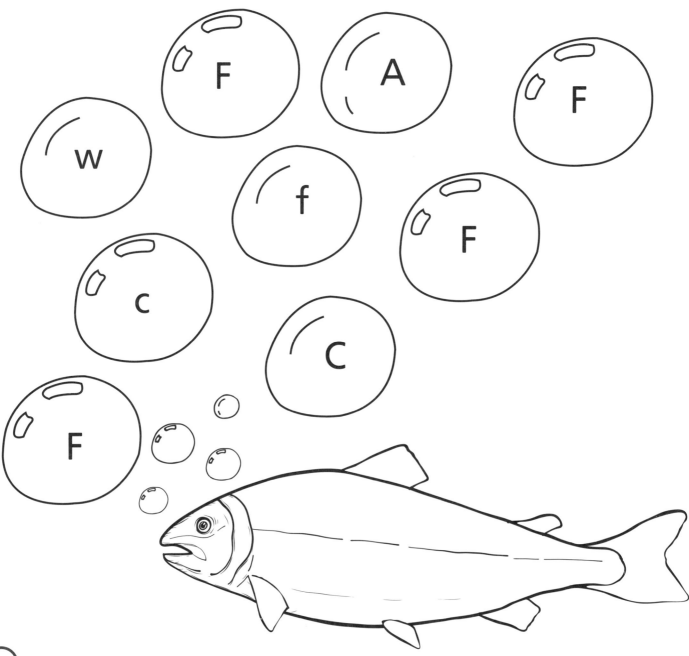

f

Read **lowercase f**.

Color the bubbles with lowercase f.

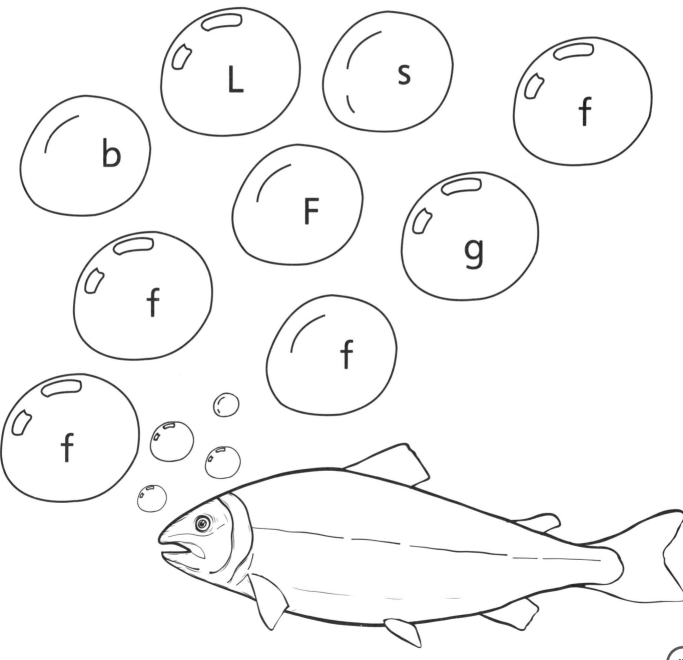

G

Read **capital G**.

Color each shape that has capital G.

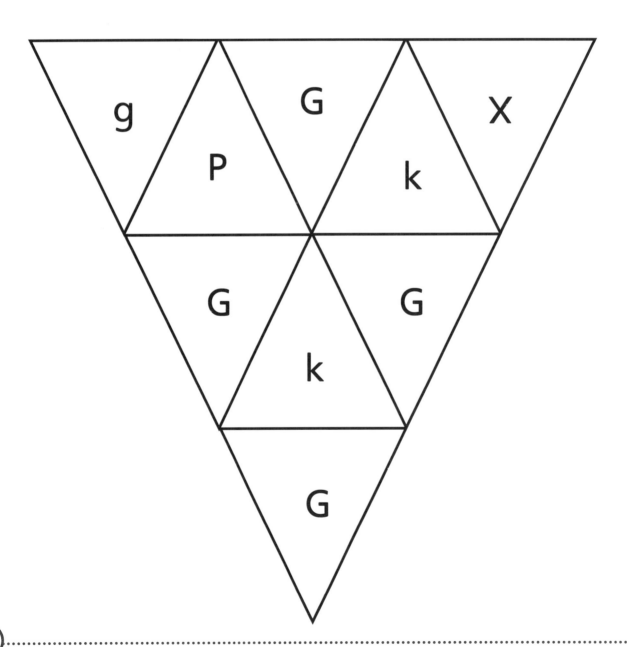

g

Read **lowercase g**.

Color each shape that has lowercase g.

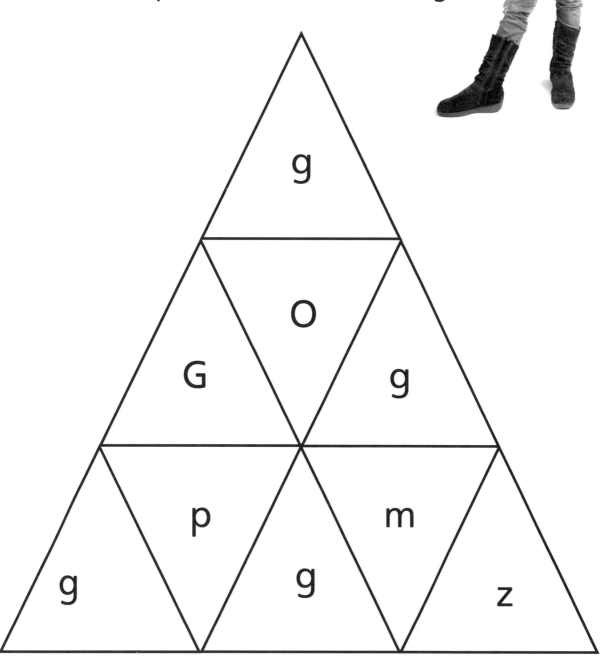

H

Read **capital H**.

Circle each capital H.
Then color the house.

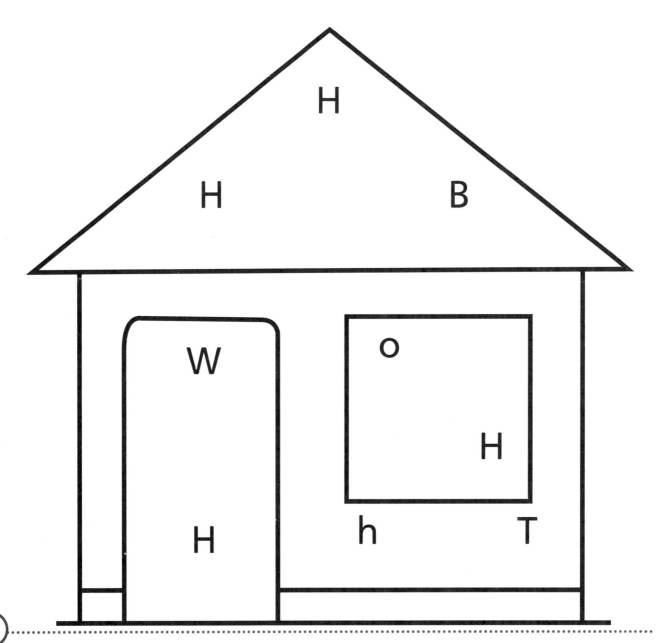

h

Read **lowercase h**.

Circle each lowercase h.
Then color the house.

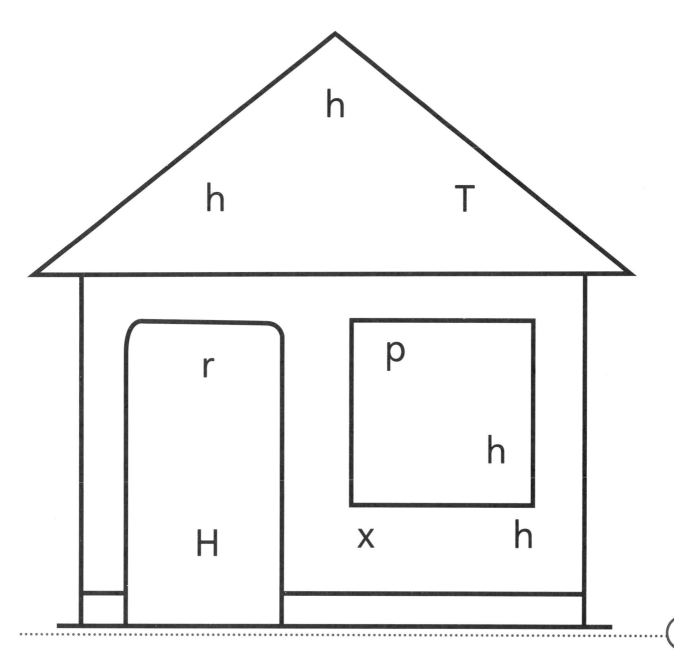

21

I

Read **capital I**.

Color the blocks with capital I.

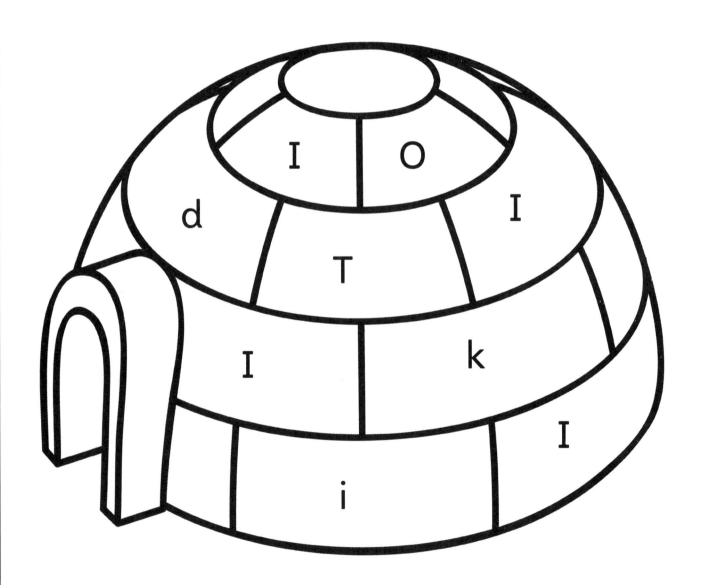

Read **lowercase i**.

Color the blocks with lowercase i.

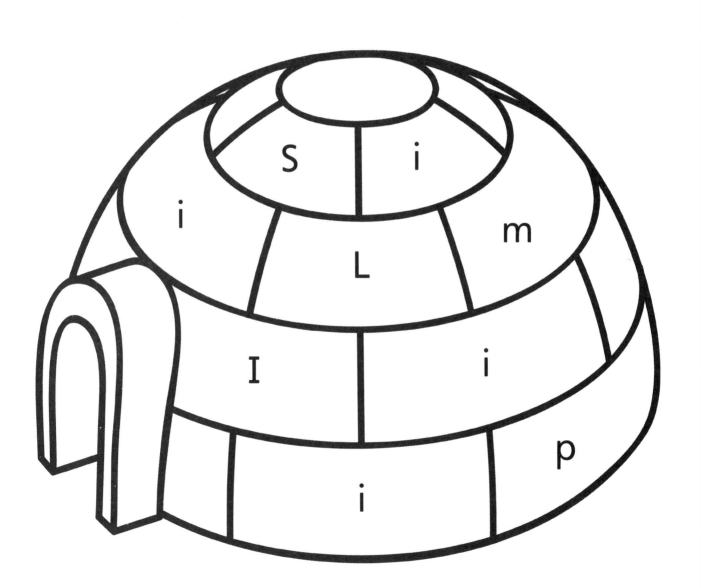

J

Read **capital J**.

Color the jars with capital J.

J   O   J

N   j   b

J   Y   J

j

Read **lowercase j**.

Color the jars with lowercase j.

L	j	f
j	J	j
k	j	m

K

Read **capital K**.

Color each cloud that has capital K.

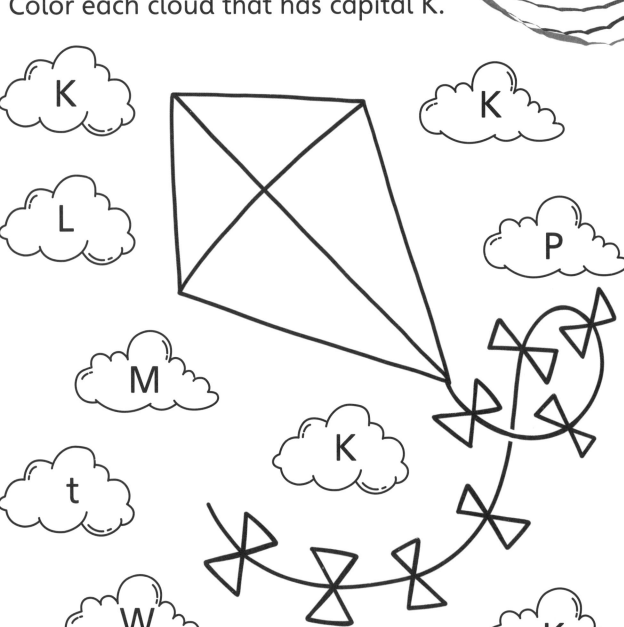

k

Read **lowercase k**.

Color each cloud that has lowercase k.

L

Read **capital L**.

Circle each capital L. Then color the leaf.

l

Read **lowercase l**.

Circle each lowercase l. Then color the leaf.

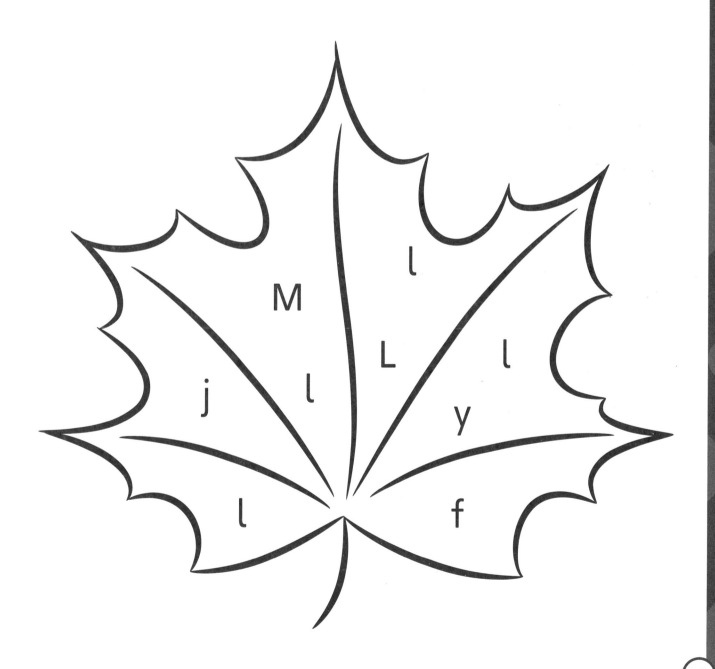

M

Read **capital M**.

Color the monkeys with capital M.

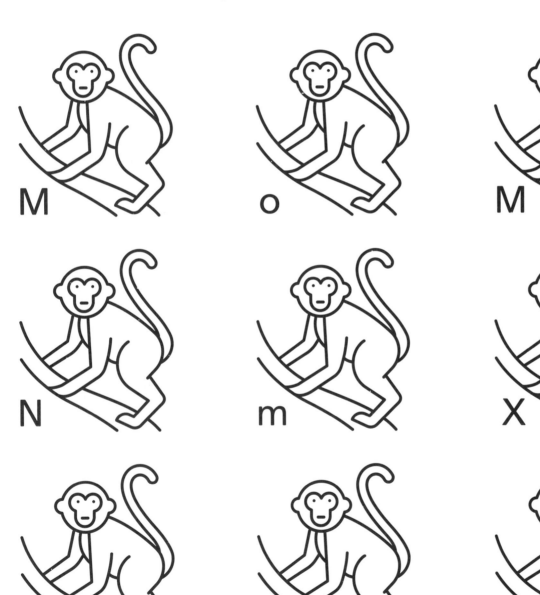

M   o   M

N   m   X

M   Z   M

m

Read **lowercase m**.

Color the monkeys with lowercase m.

N

m

e

m

M

m

u

m

P

N

Read **capital N**.

Color each fish that has capital N.

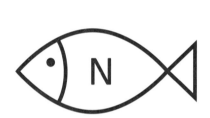 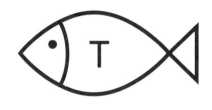 

  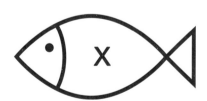

n

Read **lowercase n**.

Color each ball that has lowercase n.

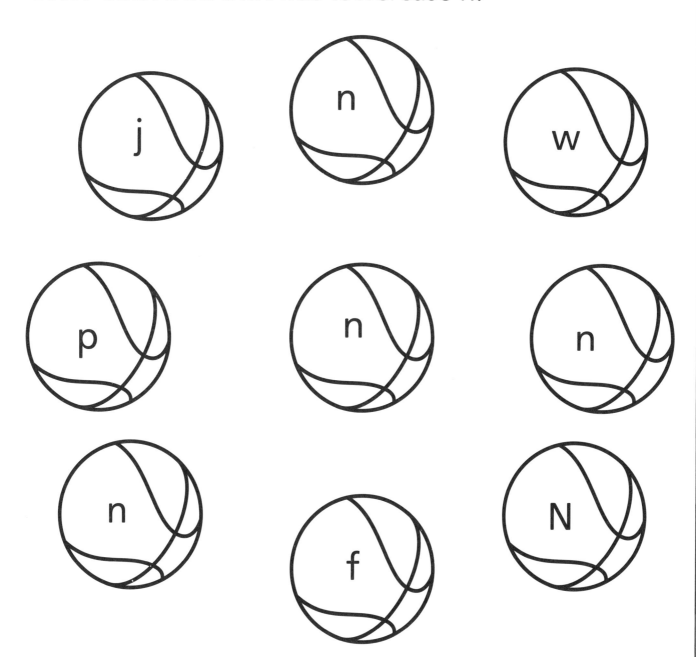

O

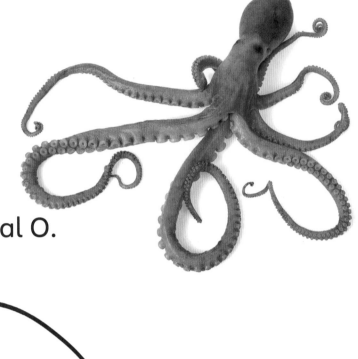

Read **capital O**.

Color the arms with capital O.

O

Read **lowercase o**.

Color the arms with lowercase o.

P

Read **capital P**.

Color the popcorn with capital P.

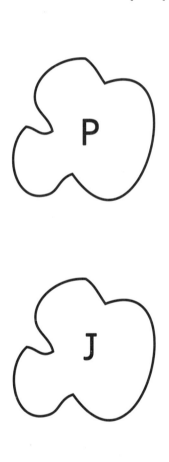

P

C

P

J

F

n

P

V

P

p

Read **lowercase p**.

Color the popcorn with lowercase p.

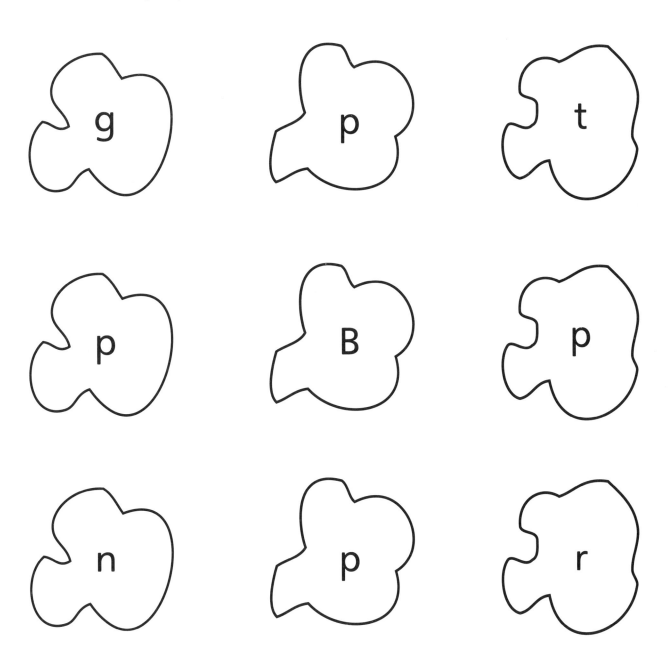

Q

Read **capital Q**.

Color each crown that has capital Q.

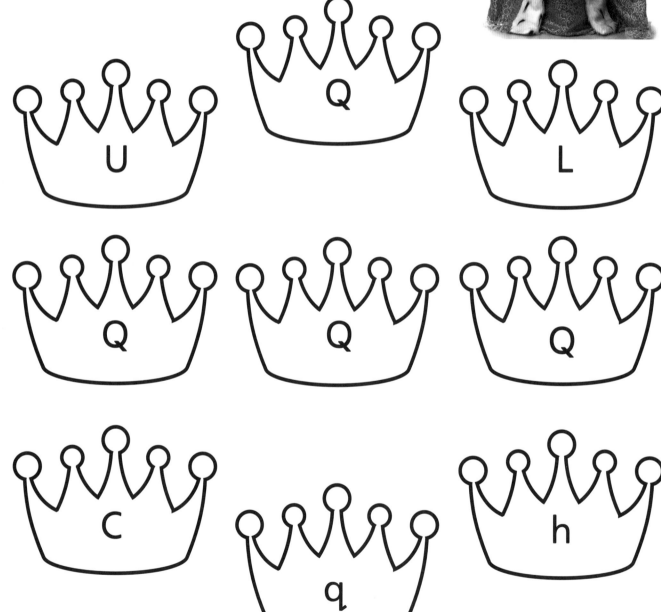

U

Q

L

Q

Q

Q

C

q

h

q

Read **lowercase q**.

Color each flower that has lowercase q.

R

Read **capital R**.

Color the parts with capital R.

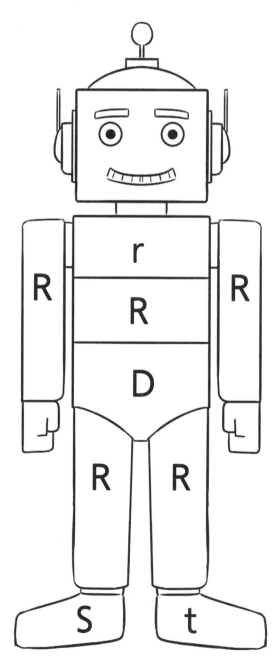

r

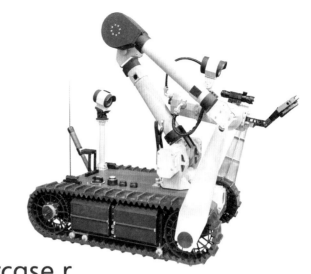

Read **lowercase r**.

Color the parts with lowercase r.

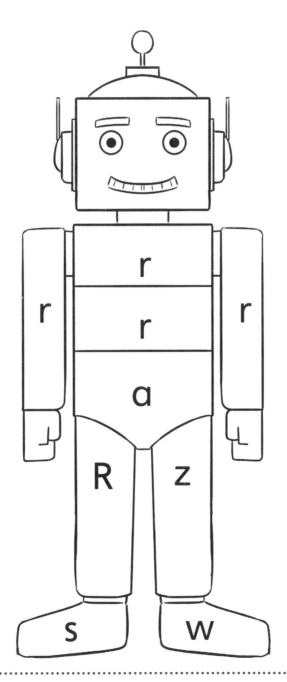

S

Read **capital S**.

Circle each capital S. Then color the sunflower.

S

Read **lowercase s**.

Circle each lowercase s. Then color the sunflower.

T

Read **capital T**.

Color the turtles with capital T.

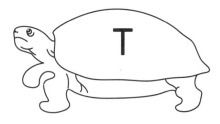  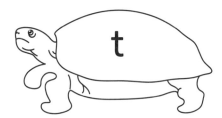

 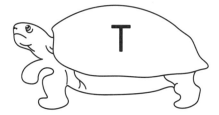 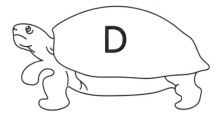

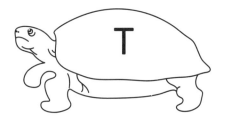 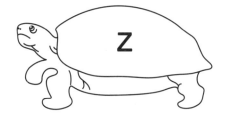 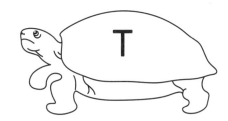

t

Read **lowercase t**.

Color the turtles with lowercase t.

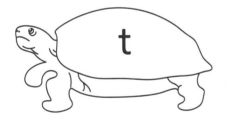

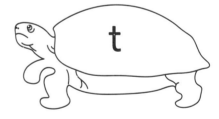

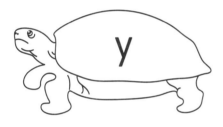

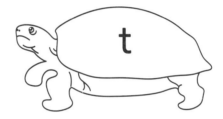

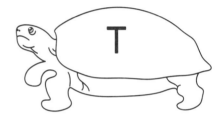

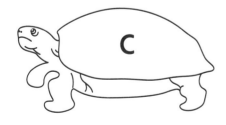

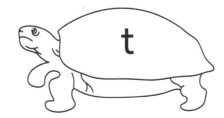

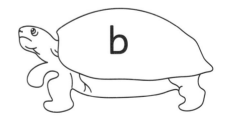

U

Read **capital U**.

Color each raindrop that has capital U.

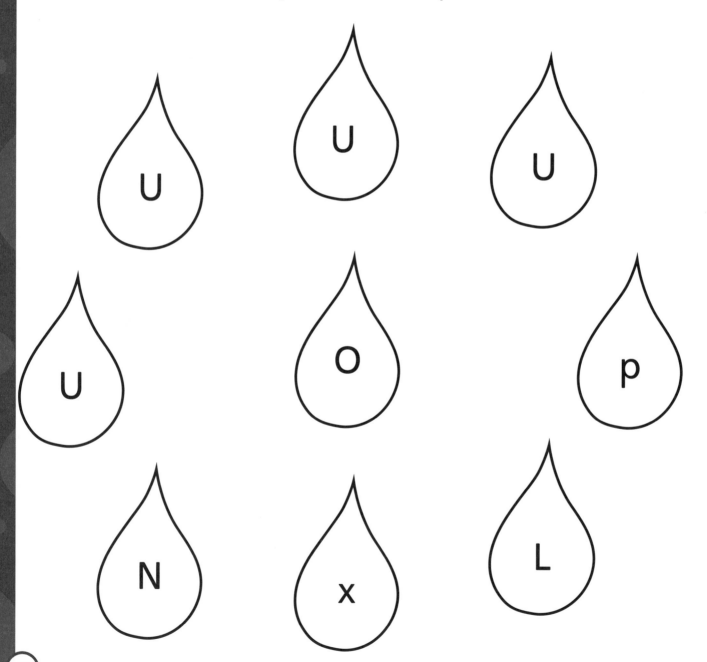

u

Read **lowercase u**.

Color each cloud that has lowercase u.

V

Read **capital V**.

Color the parts with capital V.

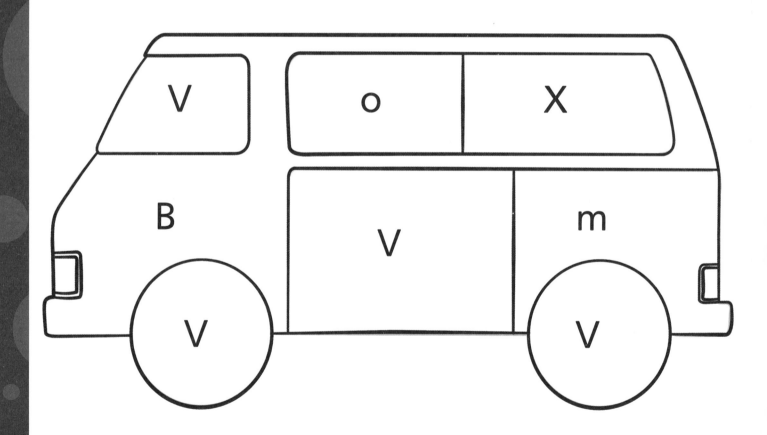

V

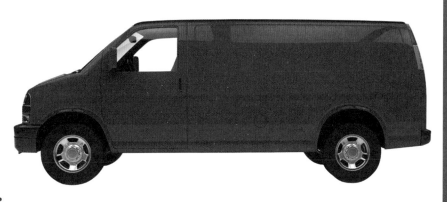

Read **lowercase v**.

Color the parts with lowercase v.

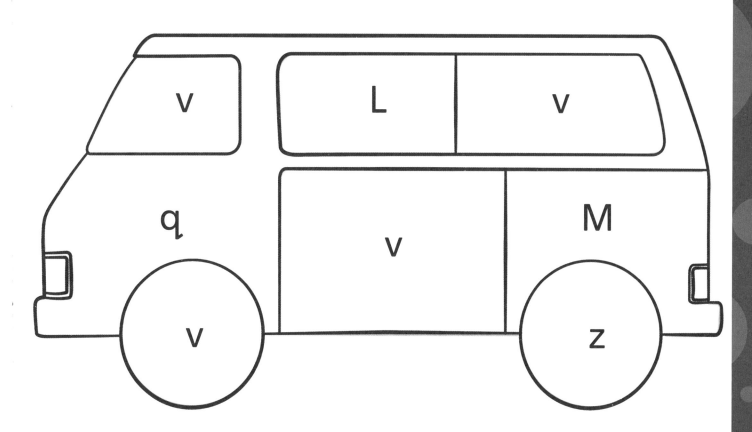

W

Read **capital W**.

Color each wheel that has capital W.

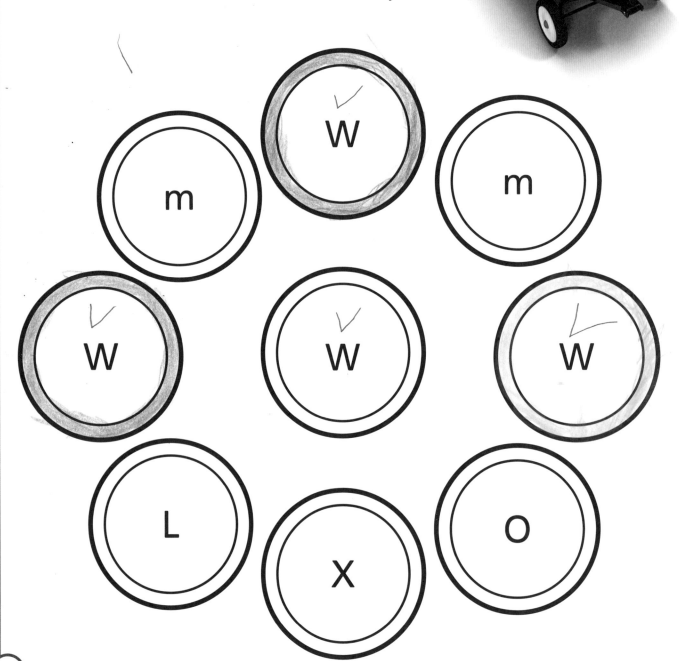

w

Read **lowercase w**.

Color each rectangle that has lowercase w.

w	c	W
B	N	x
w	w	a

X

Read **capital X**.

Circle each capital X. Then color the box.

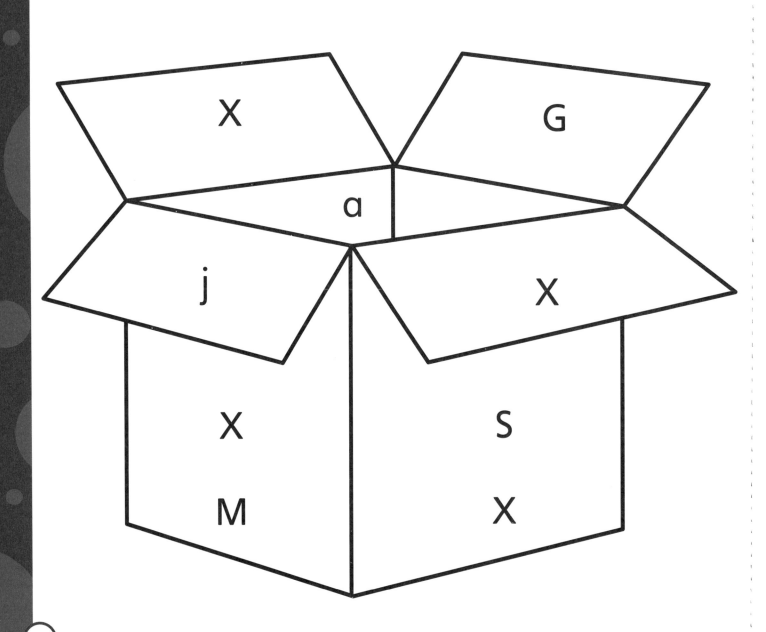

X

G

a

j

X

X

S

M

X

X

Read **lowercase x**.

Circle each lowercase x. Then color the box.

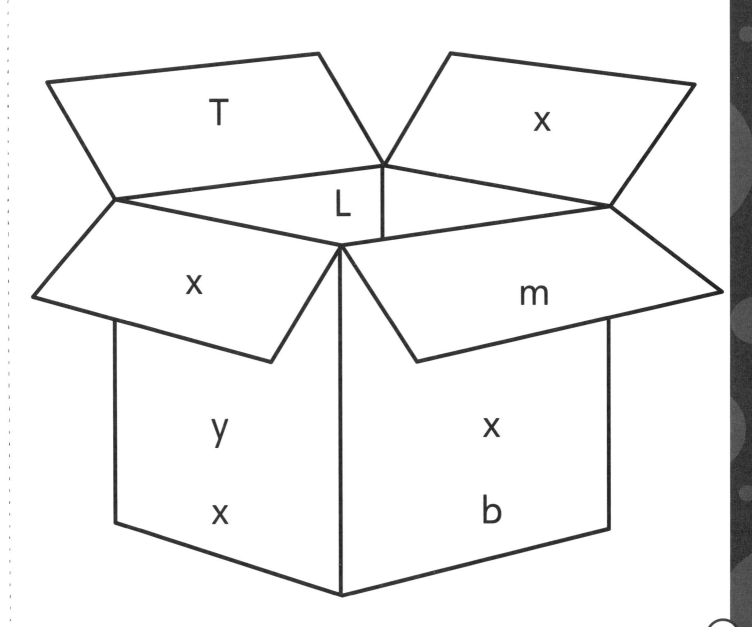

T x

L

x m

y x

x b

Y

Read **capital Y**.

Color the yo-yos with capital Y.

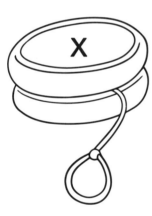  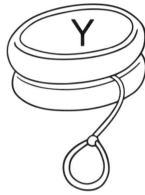

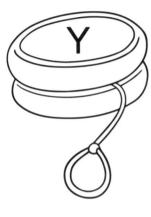 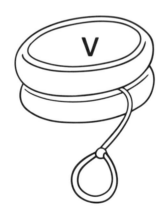 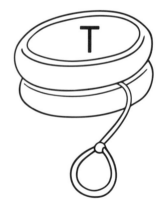

y

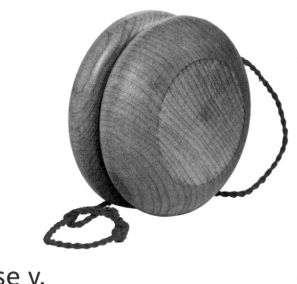

Read **lowercase y**.

Color the yo-yos with lowercase y.

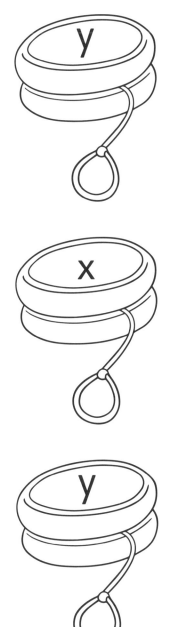
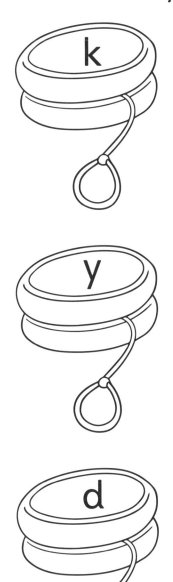
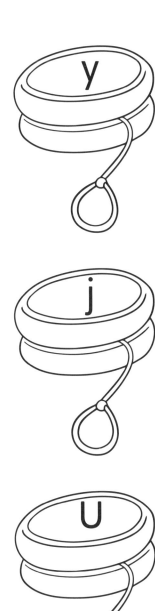

y   k   y

x   y   j

y   d   U

Z

Read **capital Z**.

Color the stripes with capital Z.

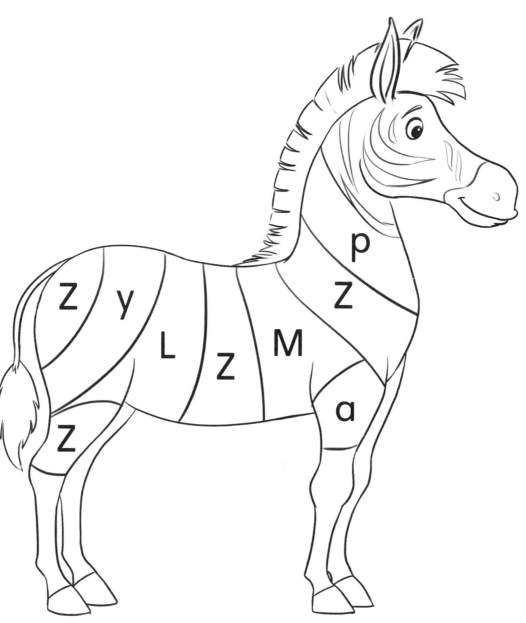

z

Read **lowercase z**.

Color the stripes with lowercase z.

Capital and Lowercase Match-up

Read the capital letters and lowercase letters.
Draw a line to match each pair.

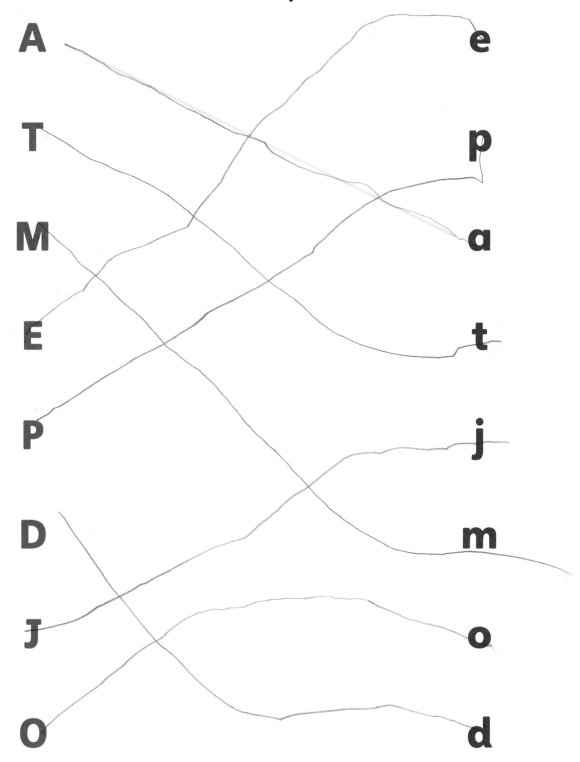

A   e

T   p

M   a

E   t

P   j

D   m

J   o

O   d

Saying ABCs

USING THIS SECTION

In these pages, children will learn the sounds that letters make. For most letters, they will see pictures that begin with the letter. Notice that the page for X uses ending sounds; this is to allow children to hear the usual sound of the letter, not the sound that it makes in words such as *X-ray* and *xylophone*. On pages that involve coloring, remember to encourage your child to follow the instructions first. After the targeted pictures or shapes have been colored, you can suggest that your child use different colors for any additional coloring.

Aa
as in apple

Say **apple**.

Apple begins with the /ă/ sound.

Say the word for each picture.

Circle those that begin like apple.

Bb
as in ball

Say **ball**.

Ball begins with the /b/ sound.

Say the word for each picture.

Color those that begin like ball.

Cc
as in cat

Say **cat**.

Cat begins with the /k/ sound.

Say the word for each picture.

Draw lines from **C** to those that begin like cat.

C

Dd
as in duck

Say **duck**.

Duck begins with the /d/ sound.

Say the word for each picture.

Color those that begin like duck.

Did you know?
Ducks have **webbed feet**. These feet make ducks great swimmers!

Ee
as in egg

Say **egg**.

Egg begins with the /ĕ/ sound.

Say the word for each picture.

Circle those that begin like egg.

Ff
as in fish

Say **fish**.

Fish begins with the /f/ sound.

Say the word for each picture.

Color those that begin like fish.

Gg

as in girl

Say **girl**.

Girl begins with the /g/ sound.

Say the word for each picture.

Draw lines from **G** to those that begin like girl.

G

Hh
as in **house**

Say **house**.

House begins with the /h/ sound.

Say the word for each picture.

Color those that begin like house.

Ii

as in igloo

Say **igloo**.

Igloo begins with the /ĭ/ sound.

Say the word for each picture.

Circle those that begin like igloo.

Jj
as in jar

Say **jar**.

Jar begins with the /j/ sound.

Say the word for each picture.

Color those that begin like jar.

Kk
as in kite

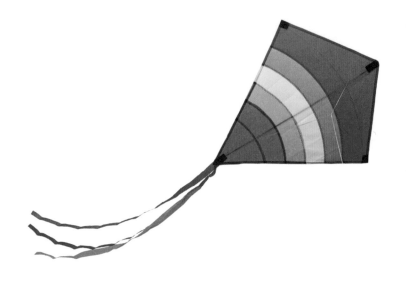

Say **kite**.

Kite begins with the /k/ sound.

Say the word for each picture.

Draw lines from **K** to those that begin like kite.

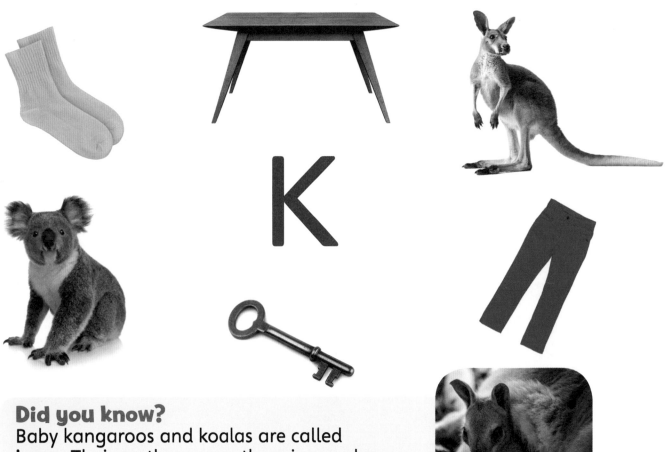

K

Did you know?
Baby kangaroos and koalas are called **joeys**. Their mothers carry them in pouches.

Ll
as in leaf

Say **leaf**.

Leaf begins with the /l/ sound.

Say the word for each picture.

Color those that begin like leaf.

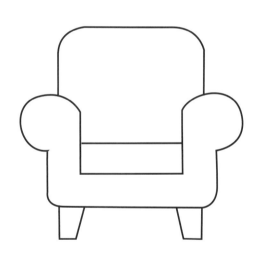

Mm
as in monkey

Say **monkey**.

Monkey begins with the /m/ sound.

Say the word for each picture.

Circle those that begin like monkey.

Did you know?
Some monkeys are big and some are small. This little marmoset can fit in a person's hand!

Nn
as in net

Say **net**.

Net begins with the /n/ sound.

Say the word for each picture.

Color those that begin like net.

Oo
as in octopus

Say **octopus**.

Octopus begins with the /ŏ/ sound.

Say the word for each picture.

Draw lines from **O** to those that begin like octopus.

Did you know?
An octopus has 8 arms. **Octo**- means 8!

Pp

as in **popcorn**

Say **popcorn**.

Popcorn begins with the /p/ sound.

Say the word for each picture.

Color those that begin like popcorn.

Qq

as in queen

Say **queen**.

Queen begins with the /kw/ sound.

Say the word for each picture.

Circle those that begin like queen.

Rr
as in robot

Say **robot**.

Robot begins with the /r/ sound.

Say the word for each picture.

Color those that begin like robot.

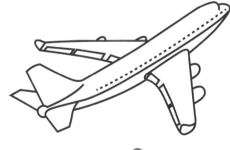

Did you know?
Most real robots do not have faces
like toy robots.

Ss
as in **sunflower**

Say **sunflower**.

Sunflower begins with the /s/ sound.

Say the word for each picture.

Draw lines from **S** to those that begin like sunflower.

S

Tt
as in turtle

Say **turtle**.

Turtle begins with the /t/ sound.

Say the word for each picture.

Color those that begin like turtle.

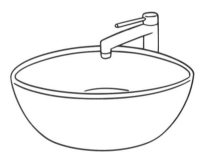

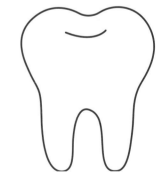

Did you know?
The leatherback sea turtle is the biggest turtle. Leatherbacks live in the ocean and lay their eggs on beaches.

U u

as in umbrella

Say **umbrella**.

Umbrella begins with the /ŭ/ sound.

Say the word for each picture.

Circle those that begin like umbrella.

Vv
as in **vacuum**

Say **vacuum**.

Vacuum begins with the /v/ sound.

Say the word for each picture.

Color those that begin like vacuum.

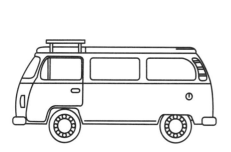

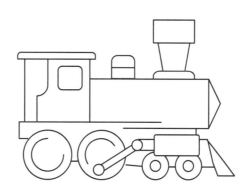

Ww

as in **wagon**

Say **wagon**.

Wagon begins with the /w/ sound.

Say the word for each picture.

Draw lines from **W** to those that begin like wagon.

W

Xx
as in the end of fox

Say **fox**.

Fox ends with the /ks/ sound.

Say the word for each picture.

Color those that have the /ks/ sound.

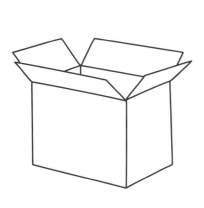

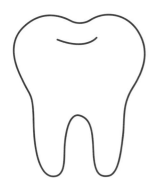

Yy

as in **yo-yo**

Say **yo-yo**.

Yo-yo begins with the /y/ sound.

Say the word for each picture.

Circle those that begin like yo-yo.

Zz

as in zebra

Say **zebra**.

Zebra begins with the /z/ sound.

Say the word for each picture.

Color those that begin like zebra.

Find the Same Sound! ....

Look at the first picture in each row.

Say the word for the picture.

Color the pictures for words that begin the same.

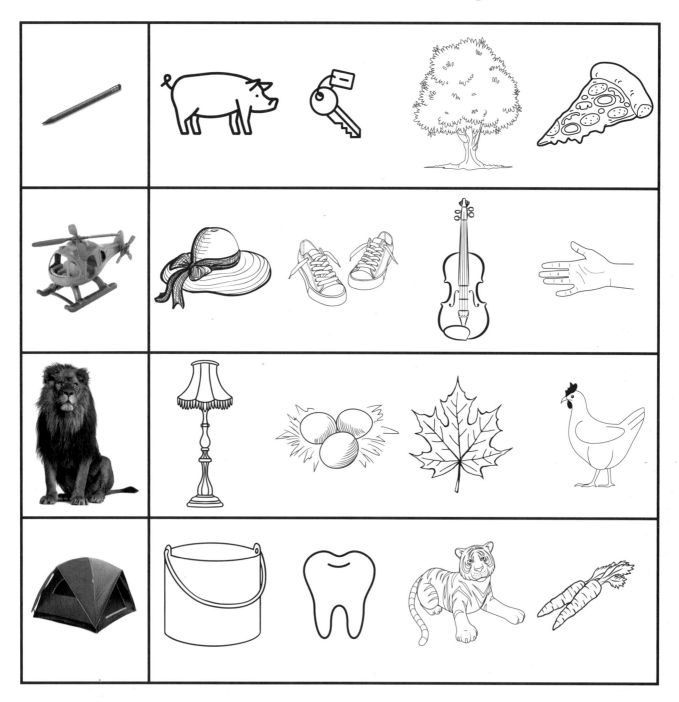

Letter Sound Match-up

Say the word for each picture.
Draw a line to its beginning letter.

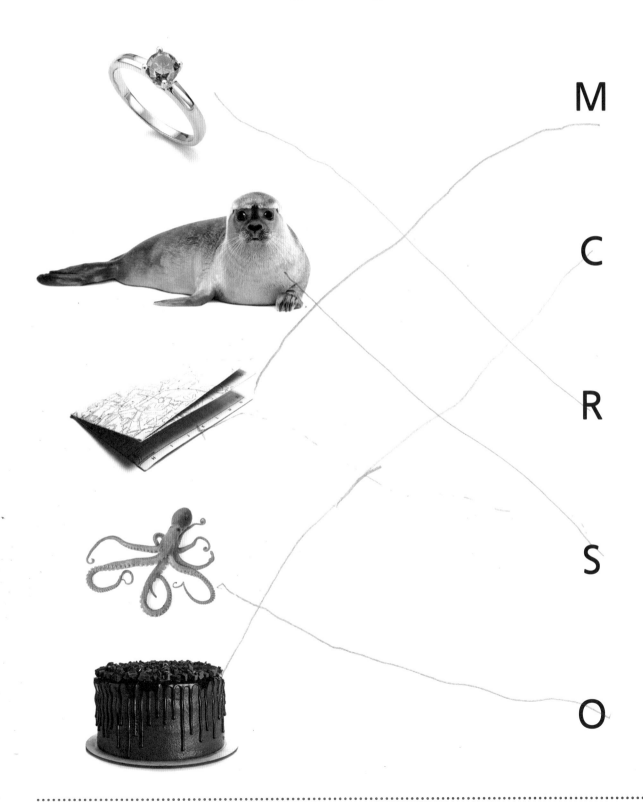

M

C

R

S

O

Letter Sound Match-up

Find the Letter!

Say the word for each picture.
What is the beginning sound?
Circle the letter.

n   i

k   g

r   d

j   x

m   b

Did you know?
Snow and ice are cold! But blocks
of snow and ice keep cold winds
out of an igloo.

Picture Pairs

Say the words for the pictures in each row.
Which two begin with the same sound?
Circle those two pictures.

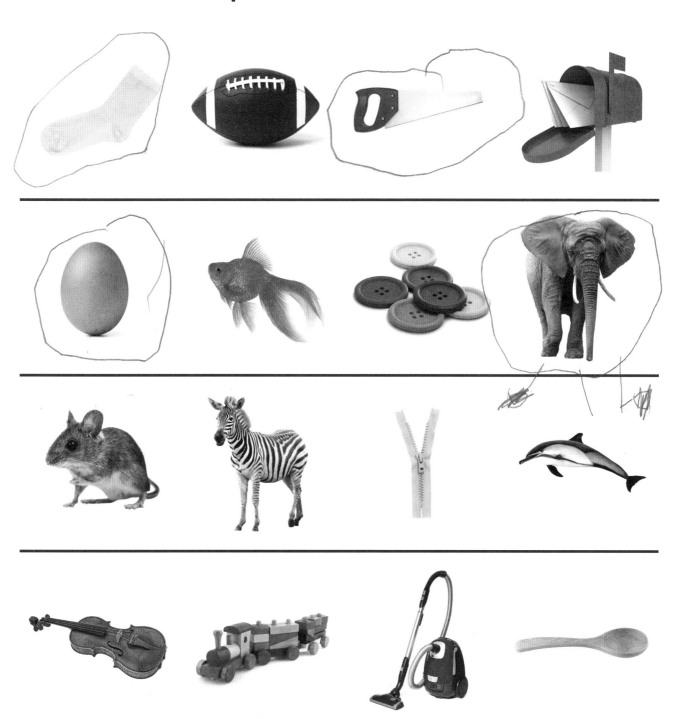

Find the Letter!

Say the word for each picture.
What is the beginning sound?
Circle the letter for the sound.

u   i

r   p

f   w

n   d

y   s

Did you know?
Penguins have wings but they don't fly. They use their wings as flippers, to swim!

More Beginning Letters ....

Say the word for each picture. What is the beginning sound? Circle the letter for the sound.

E   T   C

A   R   K

Q   B   A

G   P   M

Did you know?
Goats and sheep are part of the same animal family. But they're not exactly the same. Goats are usually more active and curious than sheep.

Your Beginning Letter! ....

What is the beginning sound of your name?
Use a sticker from the back of this book.

My name begins with this letter.

What else begins with your letter?
Draw your answer.

.... Your Beginning Letter! ....

Writing

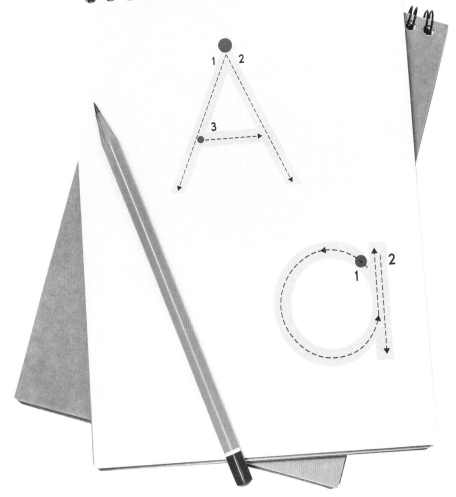

USING THIS SECTION

In the first few pages, your child will practice curves and strokes that are part of writing letters. On the alphabet and number pages that follow, have your child start by tracing the extra-large letters and numbers at the top of each page. This will help the hands "learn" the motions for each character. The starting dot shows where the writing tool should be placed onto the paper. If there is only one dot, the writing tool should not be lifted until the character is complete. If there is a smaller second dot, the tool should be lifted and replaced in the new position. Allow as much time as needed for careful tracing and writing. However, guard against frustration; remember that children's motor skills do not all develop at the same rate.

Help the rocket get to the moon.
Follow the path.

Help the rocket get to the moon.

Help the bees get to their nests.
Follow the paths.

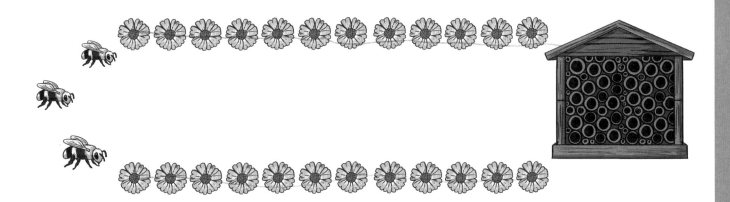

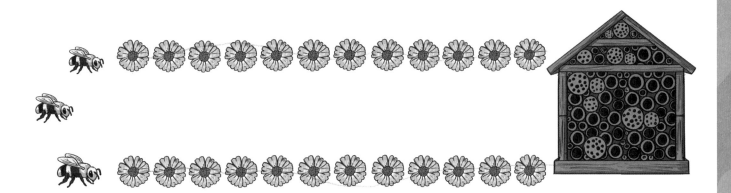

Did you know?
Bees gather nectar from flowers. They turn it into honey. They store the honey in honeycombs made of wax.

Help the frogs get to their lily pads. Trace each line.

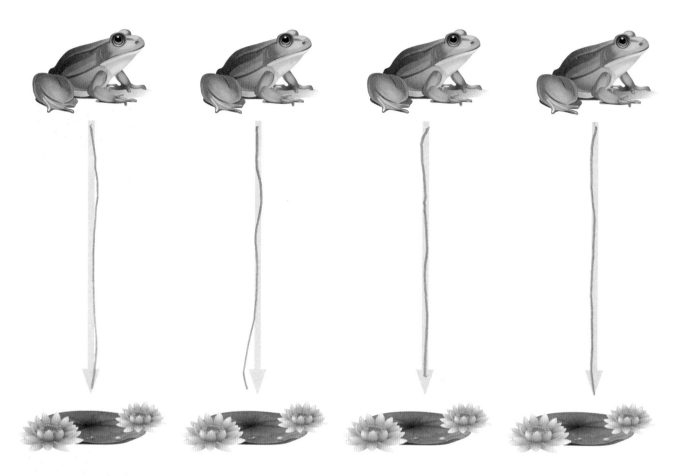

Trace each line from top to bottom. Then write your own lines.

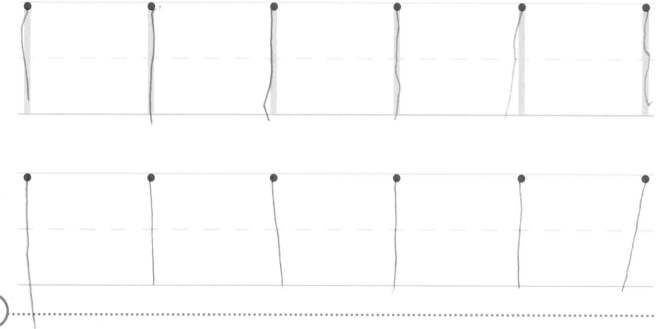

Help the butterflies get to their flowers.
Trace each line.

Trace each line from left to right. Then write your own lines.

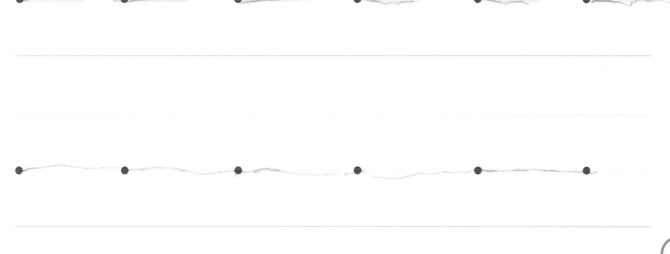

Trace each line. Then write your own.

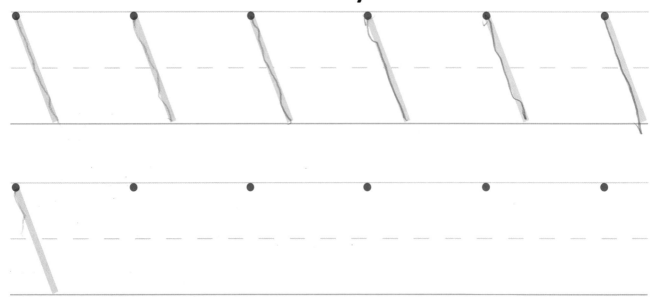

Trace each line. Then write your own.

Trace each line. Then write your own.

Help the bunnies hop to their carrots.
Trace each line.

Did you know?
We sometimes call small and baby rabbits **bunnies**. Baby rabbits are also called **kits**.

Trace each line from left to right.

Trace each line from left to right.

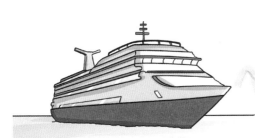

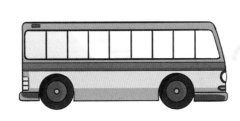

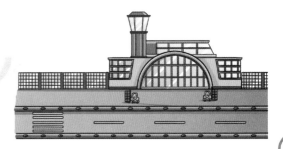

Trace **capital A.**

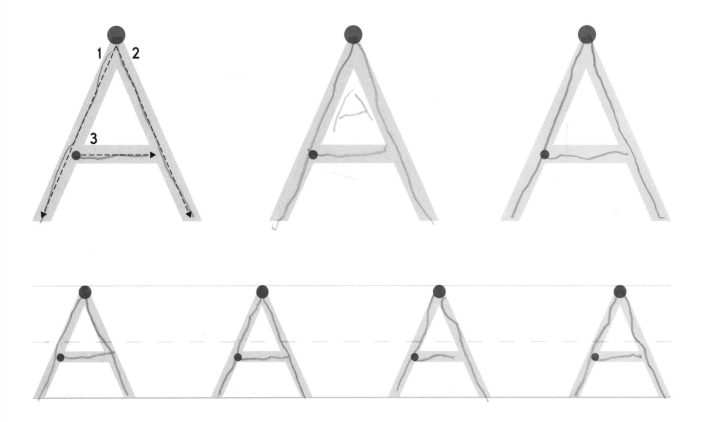

Write **capital A.**

Trace **lowercase a**.

Write **lowercase a**.

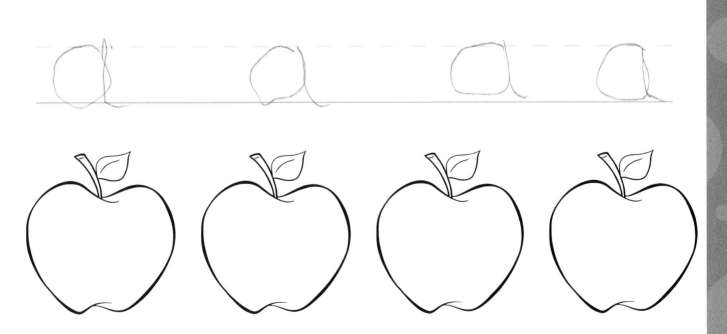

Trace capital B.

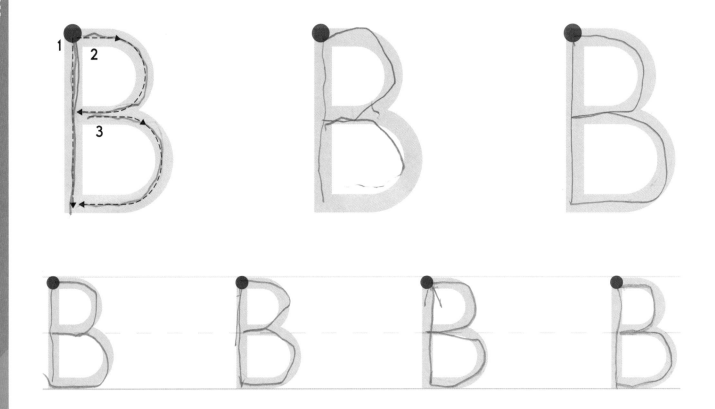

Write capital B.

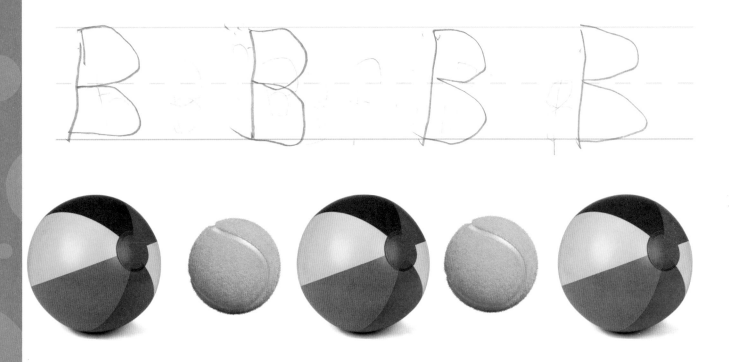

Trace **lowercase b**.

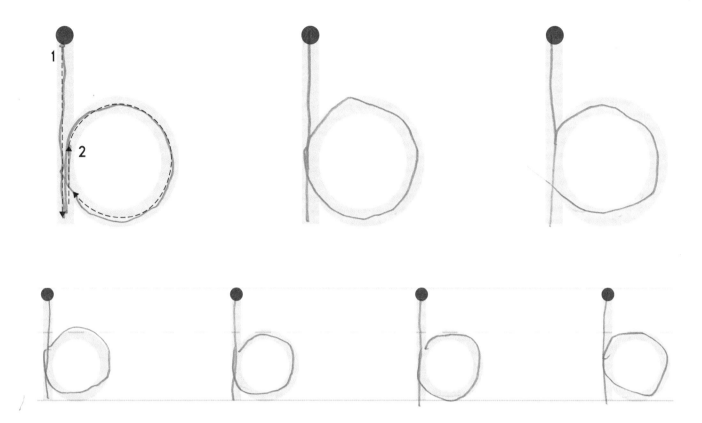

Write **lowercase b**.

Trace **capital C.**

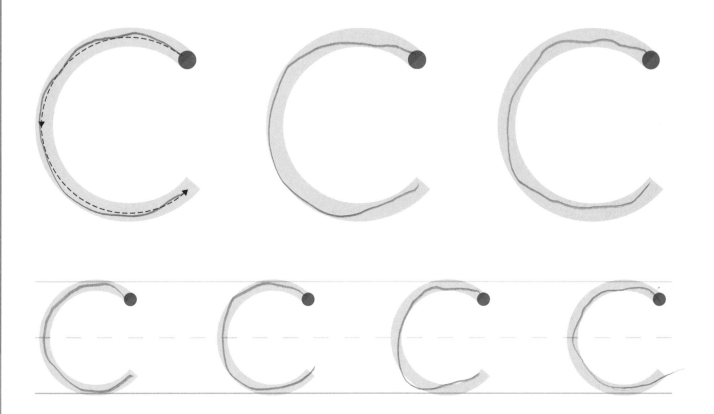

Write **capital C.**

Trace **capital C.**

Trace **lowercase c.**

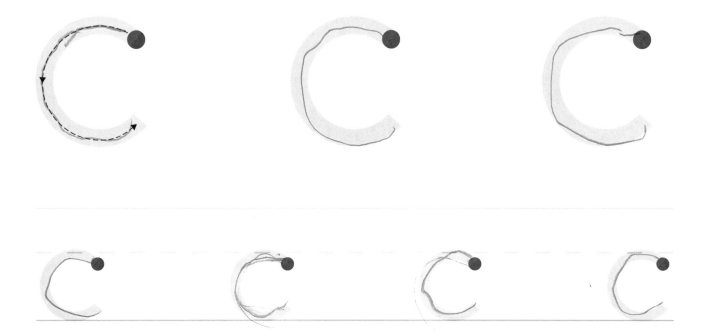

Write **lowercase c.**

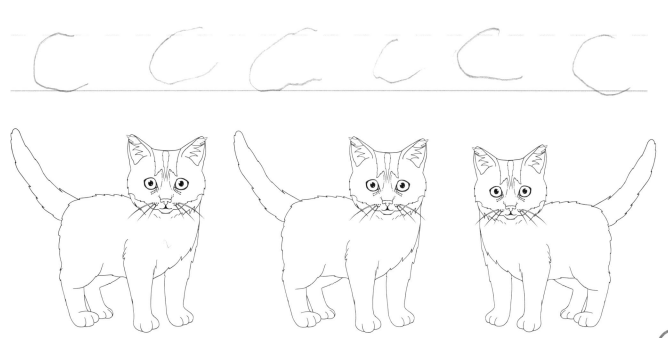

Trace **lowercase c.**

Trace **capital D**.

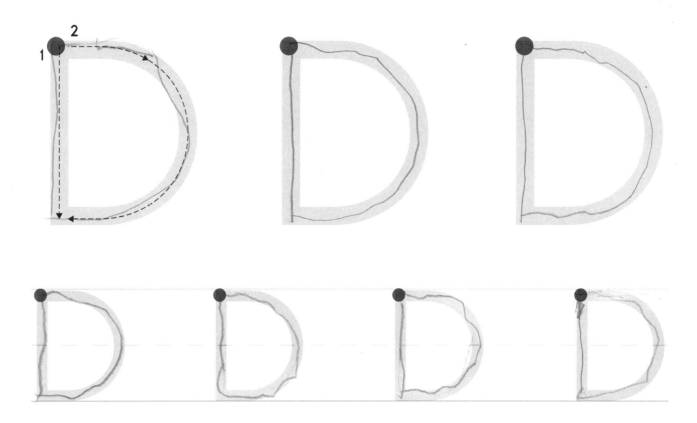

Write **capital D**.

Trace **lowercase d.**

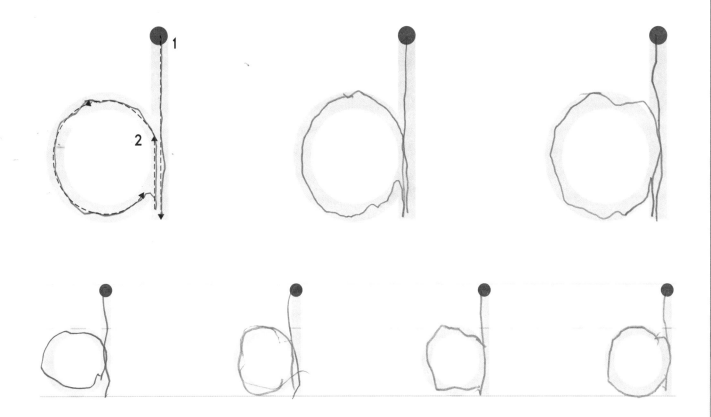

Write **lowercase d.**

Trace **capital E.**

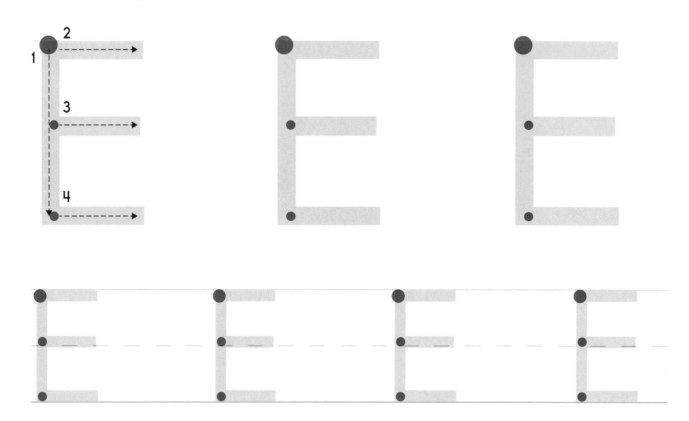

Write **capital E.**

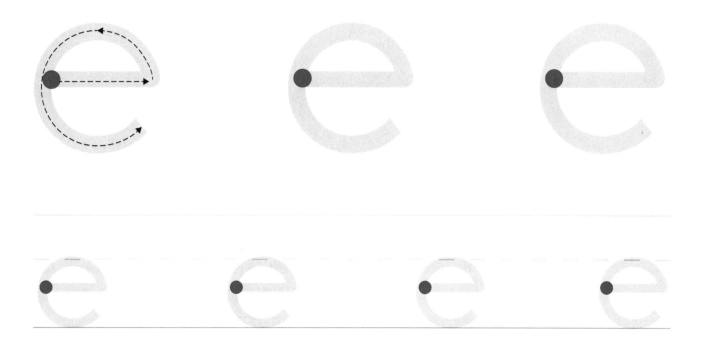

Trace **lowercase e**.

Write **lowercase e**.

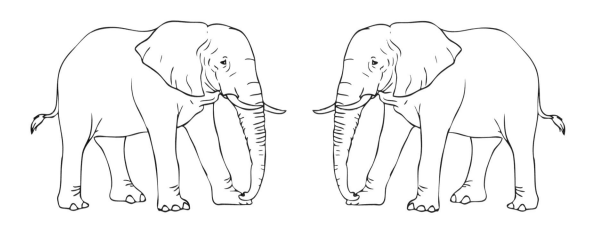

Trace **lowercase e**.

Trace **capital F.**

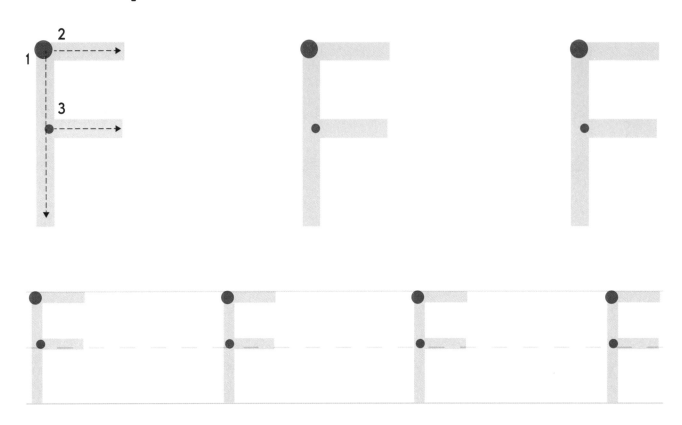

Write **capital F.**

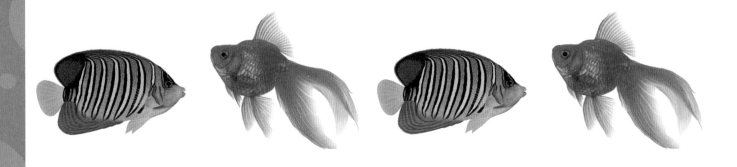

Trace **lowercase g.**

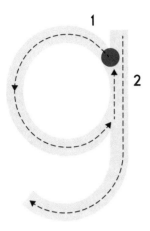

Write **lowercase g.**

Trace capital H.

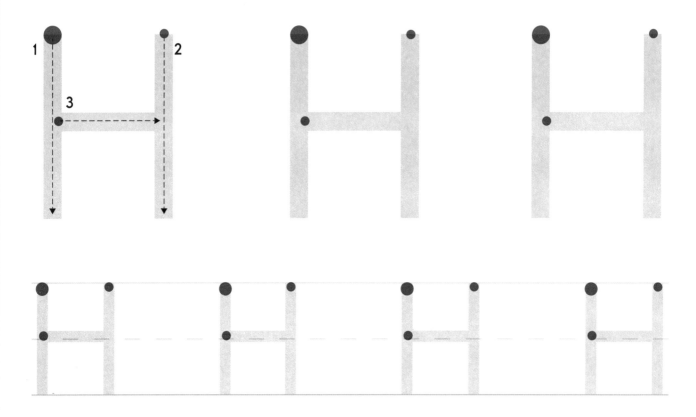

Write capital H.

Trace **lowercase h.**

Write **lowercase h.**

Trace **capital I.**

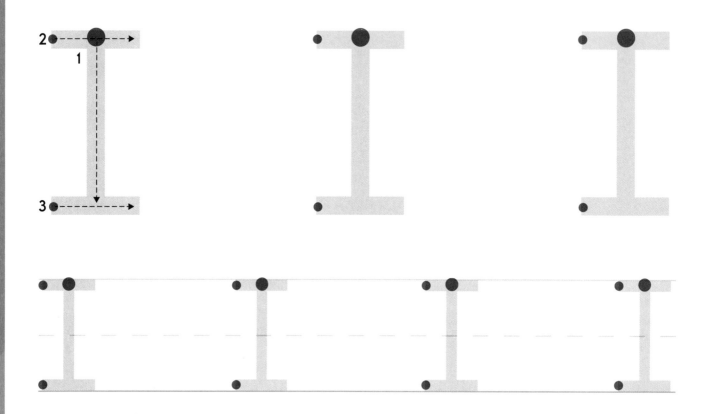

Write **capital I.**

Trace **lowercase i**.

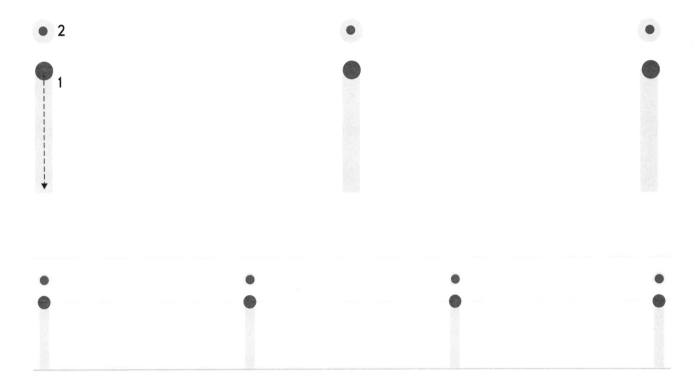

Write **lowercase i**.

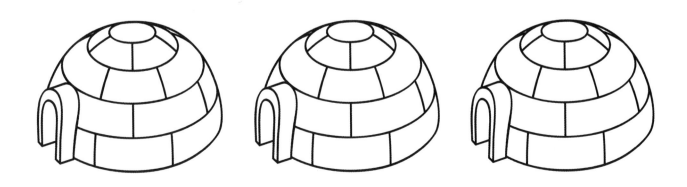

Trace **capital J**.

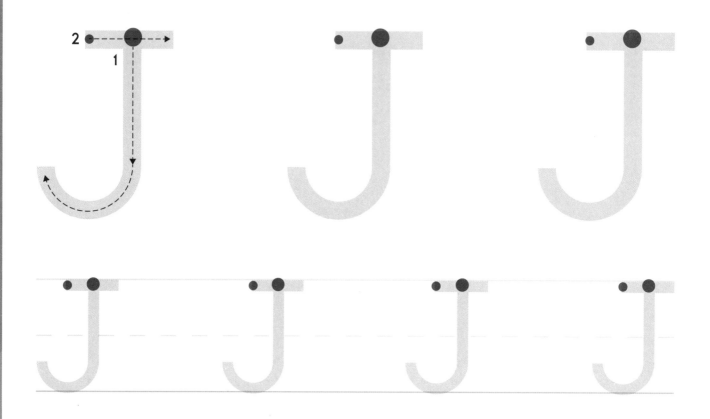

Write **capital J**.

Trace **lowercase j.**

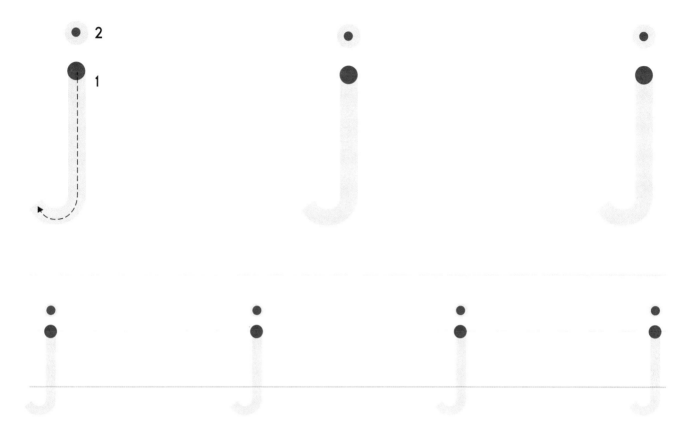

Write **lowercase j.**

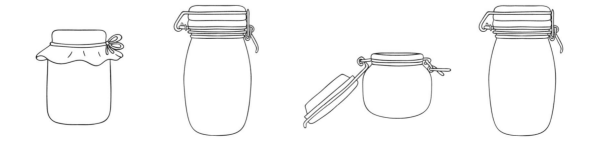

Trace capital K.

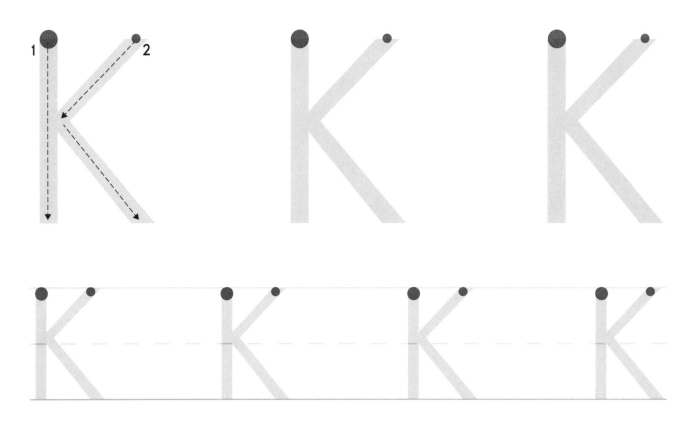

Write capital K.

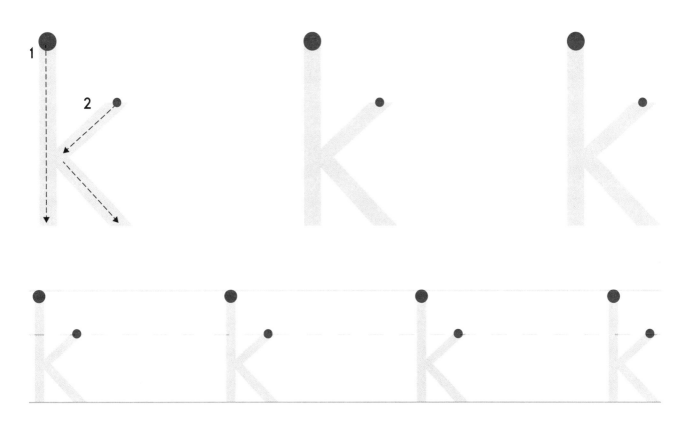

Trace **lowercase k.**

Write **lowercase k.**

Trace **capital L**.

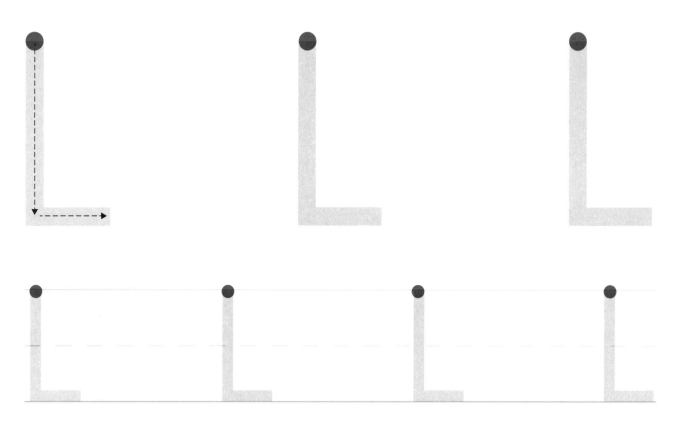

Write **capital L**.

Trace **lowercase l.**

Write **lowercase l.**

Trace **capital M.**

Write **capital M.**

Trace **lowercase m**.

m m m

m m m m

Write **lowercase m**.

Trace **capital N.**

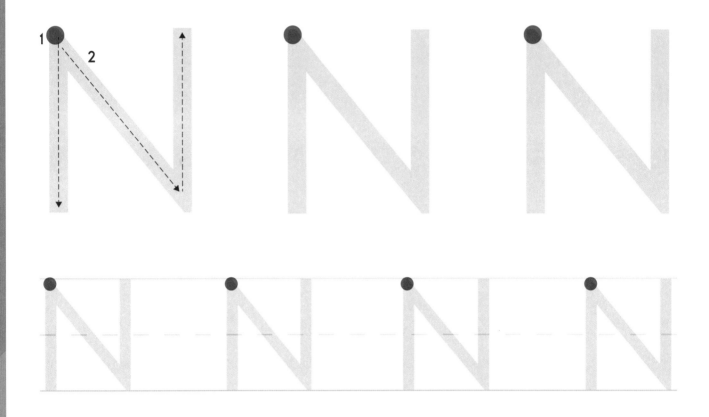

1 2

Write **capital N.**

Trace **capital N.**

Trace **lowercase n**.

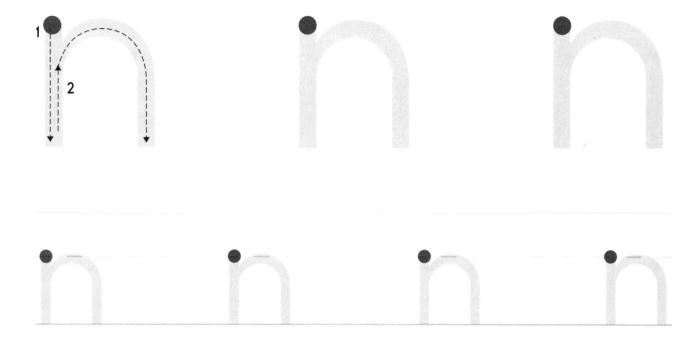

Write **lowercase n**.

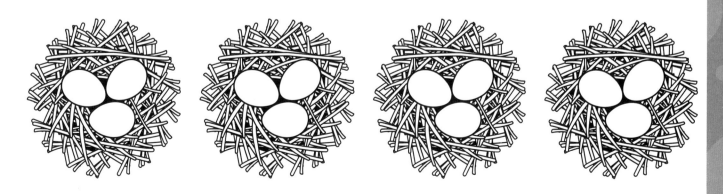

Trace **capital O**.

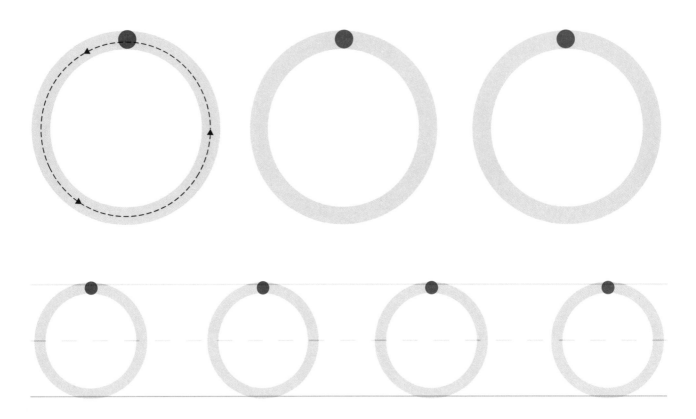

Write **capital O**.

Trace **lowercase o**.

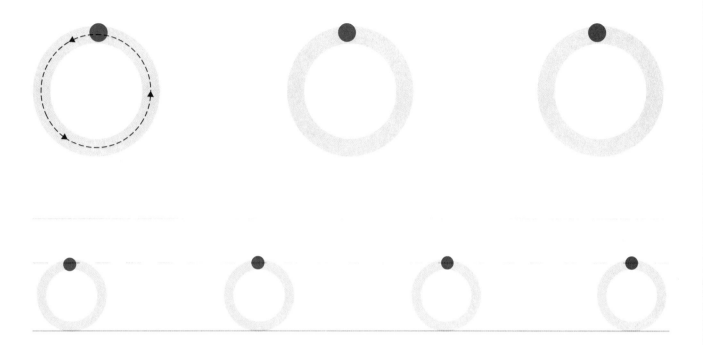

Write **lowercase o**.

Trace **capital P**.

Write **capital P**.

Trace **lowercase p.**

Write **lowercase p.**

Trace capital Q.

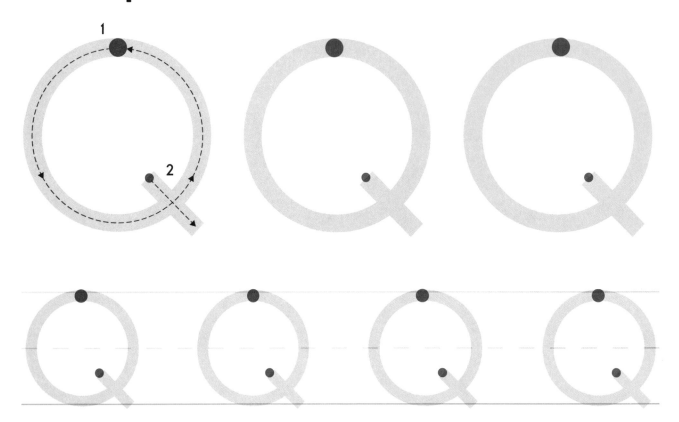

Write capital Q.

Trace **lowercase q**.

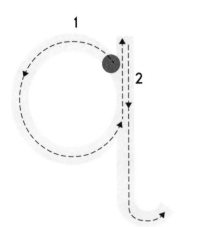

Write **lowercase q**.

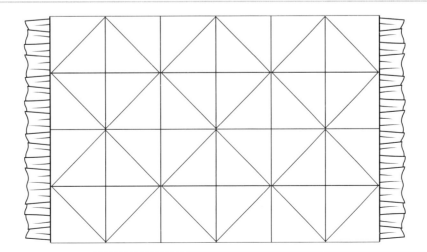

Trace capital R.

Write capital R.

Trace **lowercase r.**

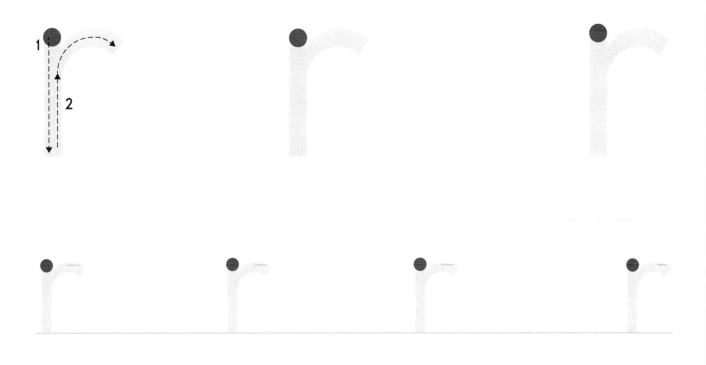

Write **lowercase r.**

Trace **capital S.**

S S S

S S S S

Write **capital S.**

Trace **lowercase s.**

Write **lowercase s.**

Trace **lowercase s.**

Trace capital T.

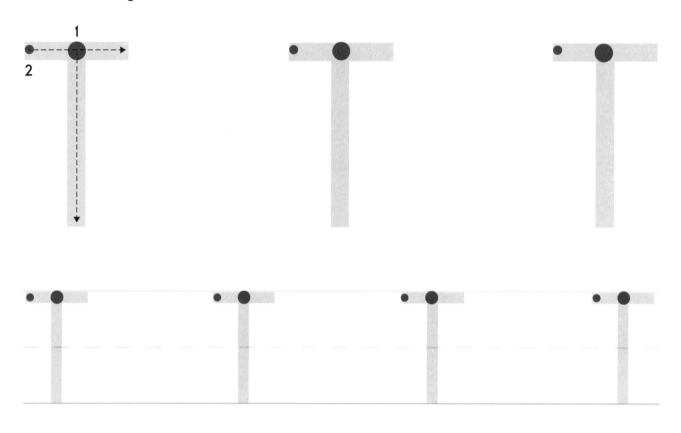

Write capital T.

Trace **lowercase t.**

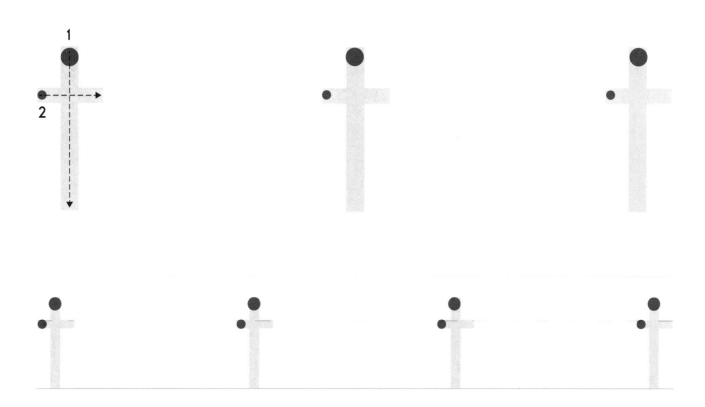

Write **lowercase t.**

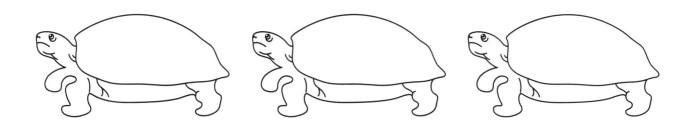

Trace **capital U**.

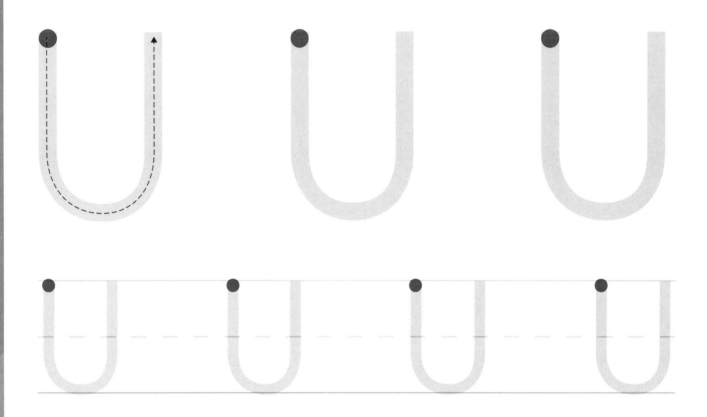

Write **capital U**.

Trace **lowercase u.**

Write **lowercase u.**

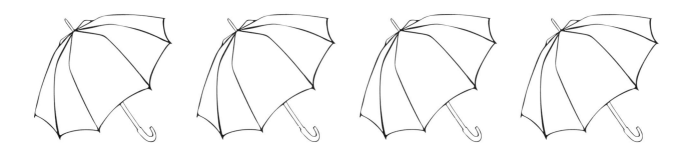

Trace **capital V**.

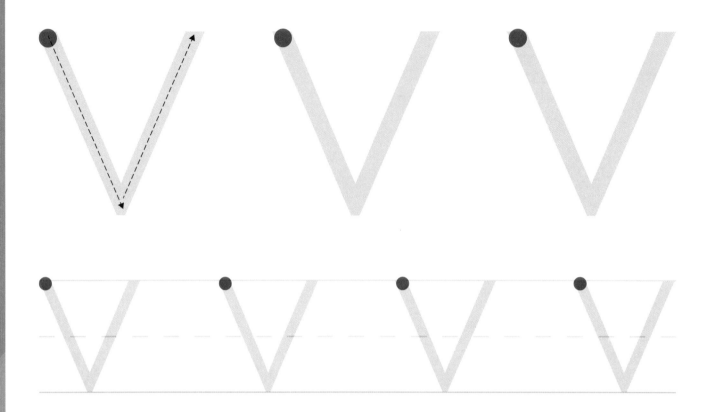

Write **capital V**.

Trace **lowercase v**.

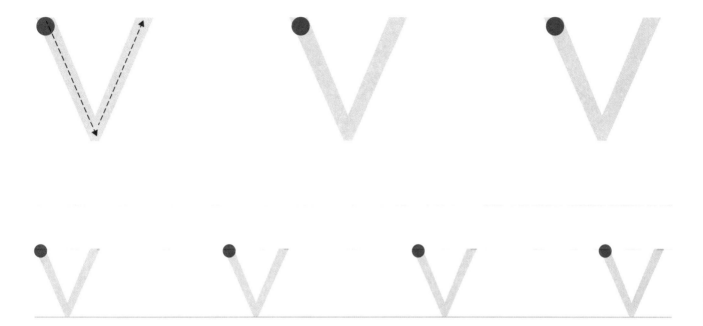

Write **lowercase v**.

Trace **capital W.**

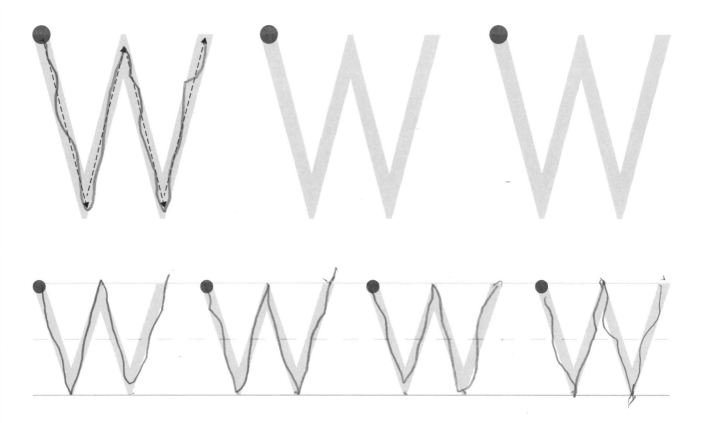

Write **capital W.**

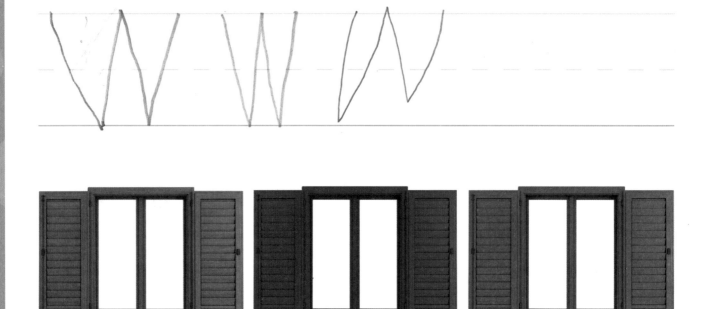

Trace **lowercase w**.

Write **lowercase w**.

Trace capital X.

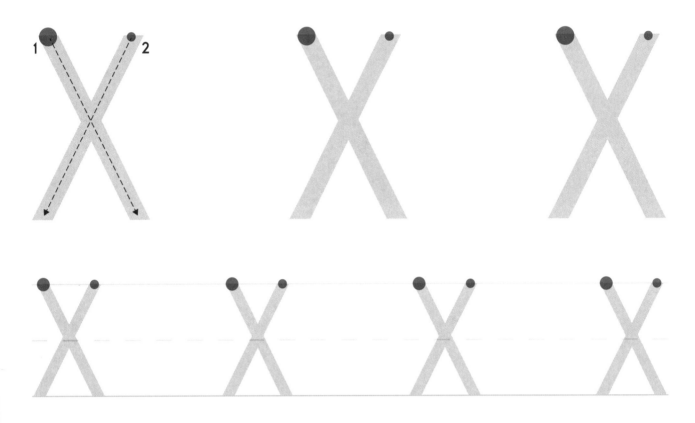

Write capital X.

Trace capital X.

Trace **lowercase x**.

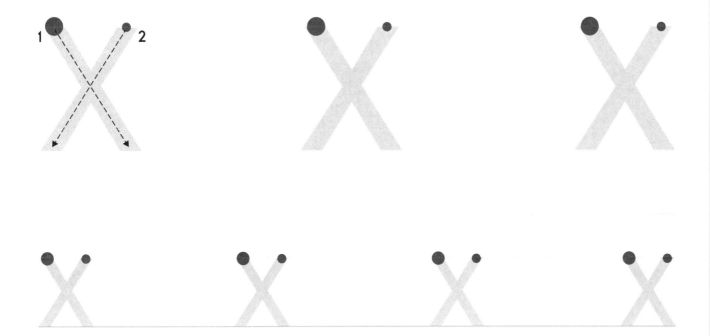

Write **lowercase x**.

Trace **capital Y**.

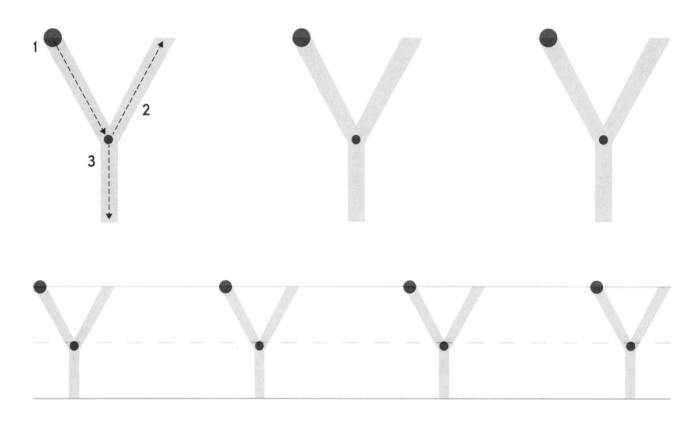

Write **capital Y**.

Trace **lowercase y.**

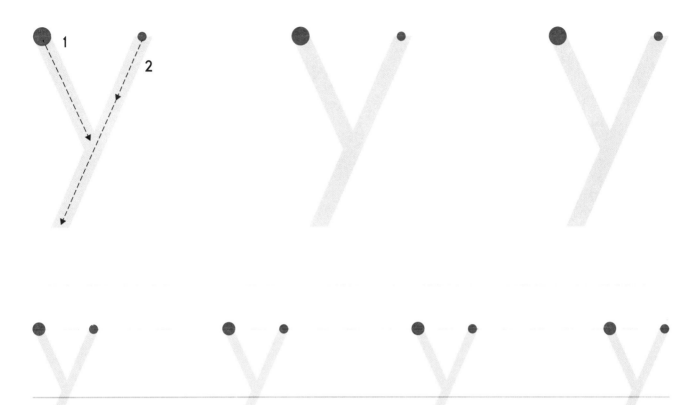

Write **lowercase y**.

Trace **capital Z**.

Write **capital Z**.

Trace **capital Z**.

Trace **lowercase z**.

z z z

z z z z

Write **lowercase z**.

Trace the number I.

one

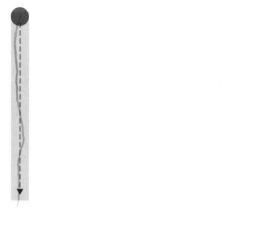  

Write the number I.

Write the number for each toy.

_____ elephant

_____ dolphin

_____ bear

Trace the number **2**.

2
two

Write the number **2**.

Write the number for each group of toys.

_____ dogs

_____ giraffes

_____ koalas

Trace the number 3.

3 three

Write the number 3.

Write the number for each group of toys.

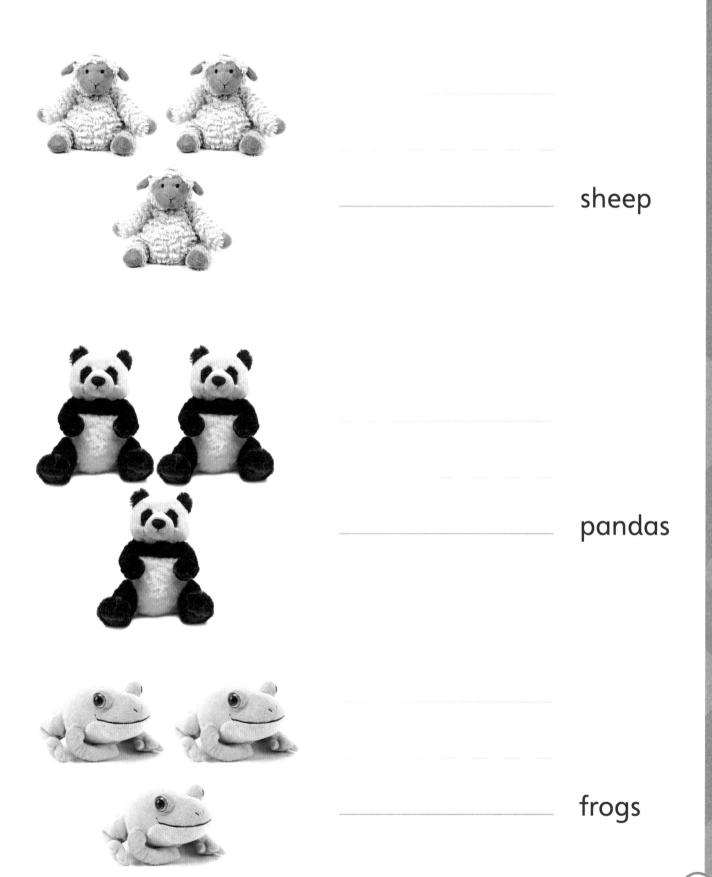

_____ sheep

_____ pandas

_____ frogs

Trace the number 4.

four

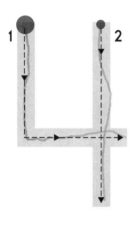 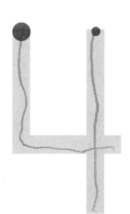 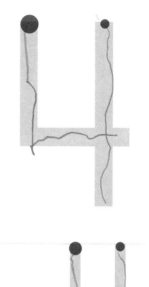

Write the number 4.

Write the number for each group of toys.

_____ lions

_____ rabbits

_____ cows

Trace the number 5.

5
five

Write the number 5.

Write the number for each group of toys.

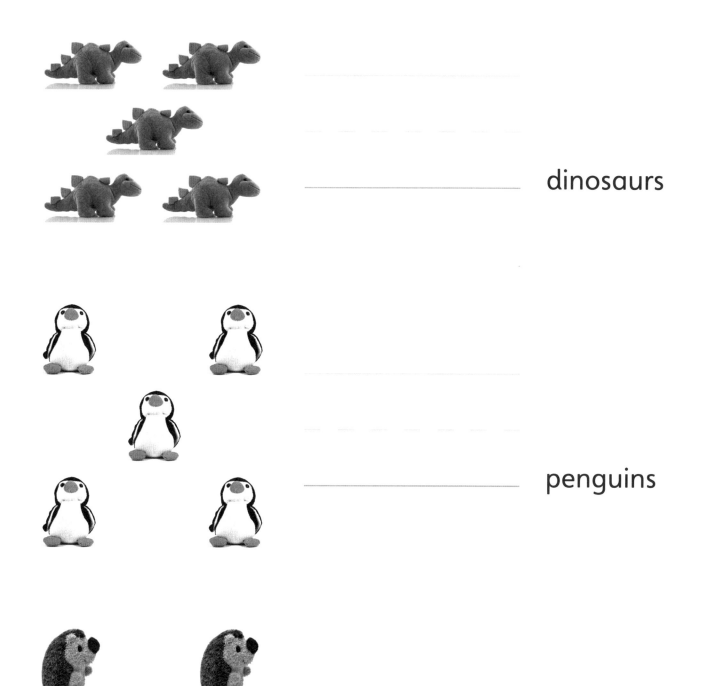

_____ dinosaurs

_____ penguins

_____ hedgehogs

Trace the number 6.

6
six

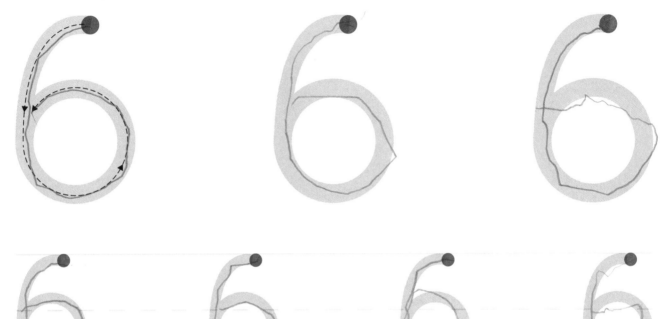

Write the number 6.

Write the number for each group of toys.

_____ cats

_____ dolls

_____ hippos

7
seven

Trace the number 7.

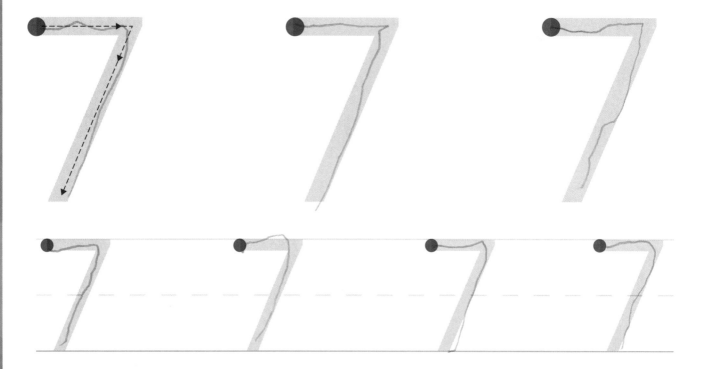

Write the number 7.

Write the number for each group of toys.

_____ tigers

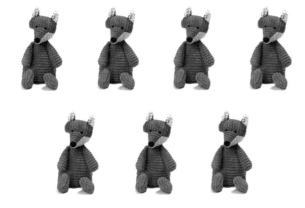

_____ foxes

_____ horses

Trace the number 8.

Write the number 8.

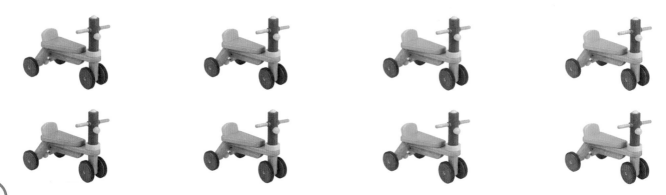

Write the number for each group of toys.

 _____ squirrels

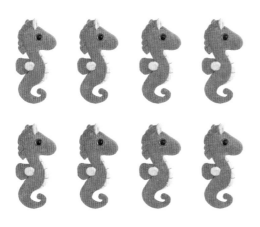 _____ seahorses

 _____ owls

q
nine

Trace the number 9.

Write the number 9.

Write the number for each group of toys.

_____ pigs

_____ kangaroos

_____ donkeys

10
ten

Trace the number 10.

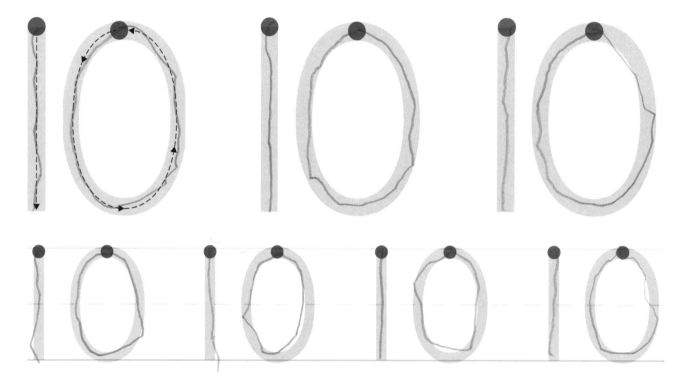

Write the number 10.

Write the number for each group of toys.

.... ducks

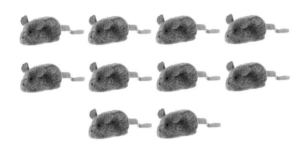

.... mice

.... chicks

How Many Animals?

Count the animals. Write the numbers.

 dog

 birds

 cats

 rabbits

 sheep

Words

hat

cat

hot

cold

Food

People eat **food**.

Circle the pictures of food.

Food

Vehicles

People ride on or in **vehicles**.

Color the vehicles.

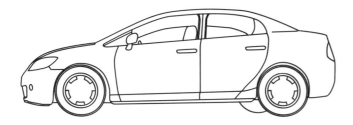

Animals

Animals are living things.

Circle the animals.

Clothing

People wear **clothing** on their bodies.

Draw lines to match the clothing to where it is worn.

Plants

Plants are living things that use sunlight to make food.

Color all the plants.

Furniture

Chairs, tables, and beds are kinds of **furniture**.

Color the furniture in this house.

Is it Food?

Draw an **X** on the pictures that are **not** food.

Is it a Vehicle?

Draw an X on the pictures that are not vehicles.

Is it an Animal?

Color each animal.

Is it an Animal?

Is it Clothing?

Color each piece of clothing.

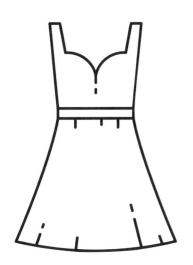

hot

Circle the things that are **hot**.

cold

Cold is the opposite of hot.

Circle the things that are **cold**.

slow

Color these slow things.

fast

Fast is the opposite of slow.

Color these **fast** things.

up

The girl is going **up** the ladder.

The boy is going **down** the slide.

The boy is **up**.

The girl is **down**.

down

Down is the opposite of up.

This boy is going **up** the stairs.

This boy is going **down** the stairs.

This squirrel is **up**.

This squirrel is **down**.

empty

Circle the things that are **empty**.

full

Full is the opposite of empty.

Circle the things that are **full**.

day

It is light during the day.

Tell what is happening in the pictures.

night

It is dark at **night**.

Night is the opposite of day.

Tell what is happening in the pictures.

happy

People smile when they are **happy**.

Circle the pictures of people who look happy.

sad

Sad is the opposite of happy.

When people are sad, their mouths turn down.

Sometimes they cry.

Circle the pictures of people who look **sad**.

big

Color these big things.

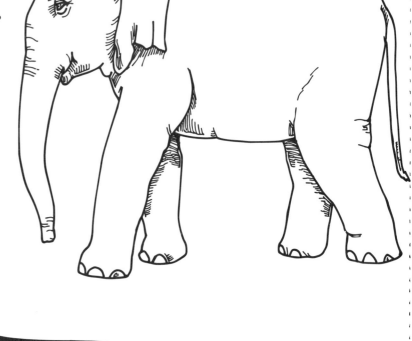

small

Small is the opposite of big.

Color these **small** things.

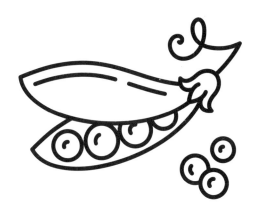

wet

Write W next to wet things.

dry

Dry is the opposite of wet.

Write D next to dry things.

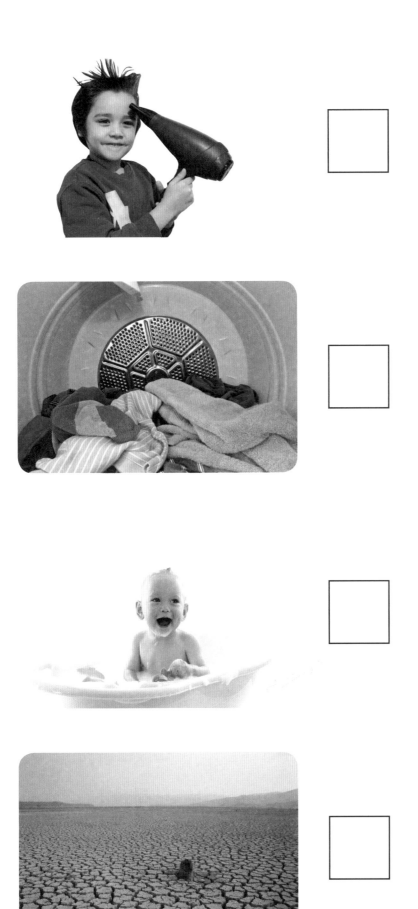

Draw a line from each picture to its opposite.

Then color the pictures.

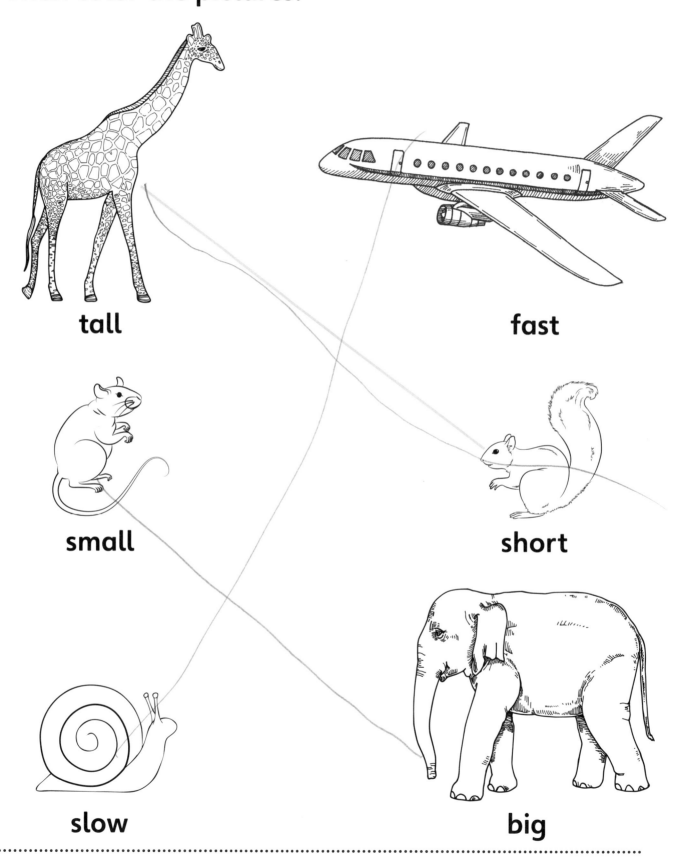

tall

fast

small

short

slow

big

Draw a line from each picture to its opposite.

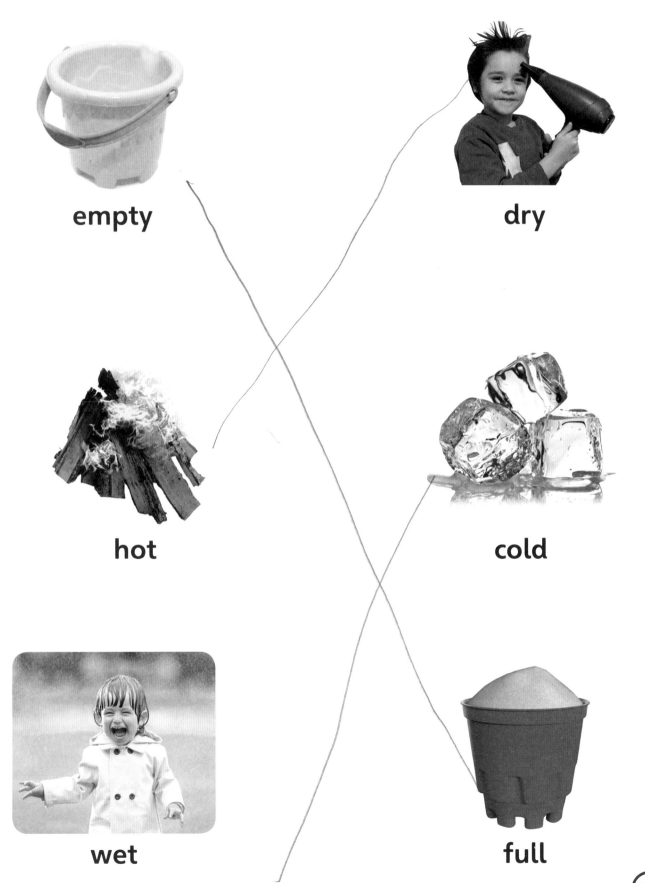

empty

dry

hot

cold

wet

full

on

The child is **on** the box.

Circle the pictures that show **on**.

next to

The child is **next to** the box.

Circle the pictures that show **next to**.

under

The child is **under** the box.

Circle the pictures that show **under**.

above

The child is **above** the box.

Circle the pictures that show **above**.

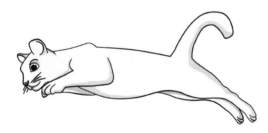

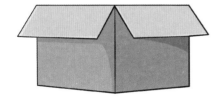

in front of

The child is **in front of** the box.

Circle the pictures that show **in front of**.

behind

The child is **behind** the box.

Circle the pictures that show **behind**.

in

The child is **in** the box.

Circle the pictures that show **in**.

....in

between

The child is **between** the boxes.

Circle the pictures that show **between**.

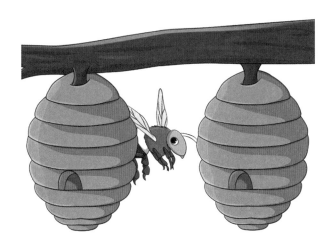

Rhyming Words

> **!** Say **hat**. Say **mat**.
> These words **rhyme**.

Say the word for each picture.

Color those that rhyme with hat and mat.

Rhyming Words

Say **rock.**

Now say the word for each picture.

Color those that rhyme with **rock.**

Rhyming Words

Rhyming Words

Say **bee**.

Now say the word for each picture.

Color those that rhyme with **bee**.

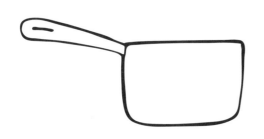

Rhyming Words

Say snail.

Now say the word for each picture.

Color those that rhyme with snail.

More Rhymes

Say the word for each picture.

Draw lines to connect those that rhyme.

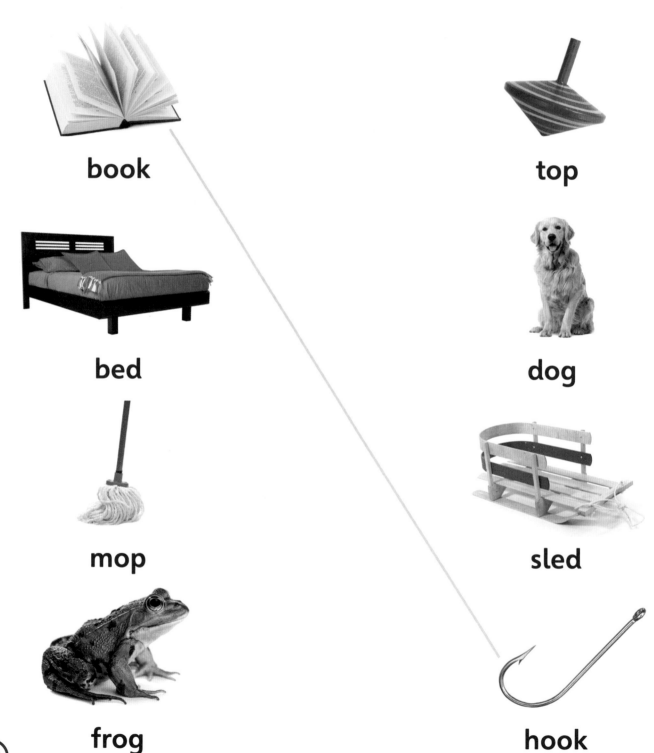

book

top

bed

dog

mop

sled

frog

hook

Rhyming Pairs

Say the word for each picture.

Color the two that rhyme.

Rhyming Pairs

Say the word for each picture.

Color the two that rhyme.

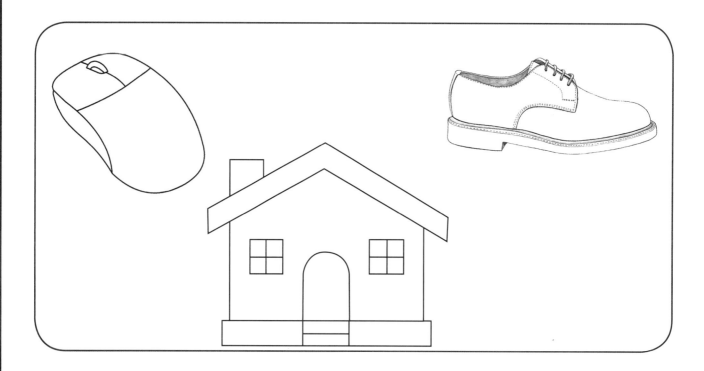

Rhyming Pairs

Colors and Shapes

Blue

This car is **blue.**

Circle the things that are blue.

Red

This star is red.

Color each star red.

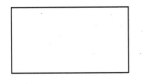   

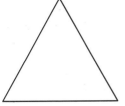   

Yellow

This bird is **yellow**.

Circle the things that are yellow.

Did you know?
A canary is a yellow bird.
Some people keep them as pets.

Green

This leaf is green.

Color each frog green.

Purple

This toy elephant is **purple**.

Circle the purple toys.

Orange

This pumpkin is **orange**.

Color the pumpkins orange.

Did you know?
A pumpkin is a squash.
You can make a pie with a pumpkin.

Brown

This sweater is **brown**.

Circle the brown things.

Colors

Draw a line to match each toy to its color.

blue

red

yellow

green

purple

orange

brown

Square

This shape is a square.

Trace each square.

Square

These shapes are squares.

Circle each square.

Did you know?
A square has 4 sides. All the sides are the same length.

Triangle

This is a triangle.

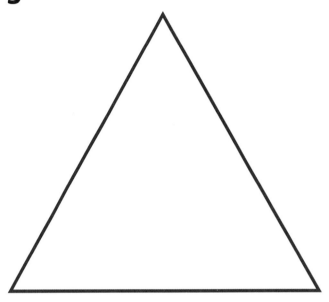

Trace each triangle.

Triangle

These are triangles.

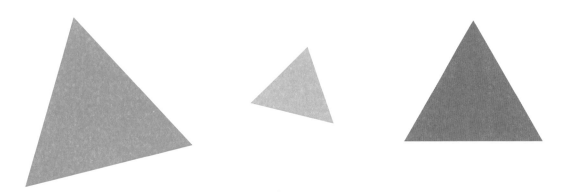

Circle each triangle.

Rectangle

This shape is a **rectangle**.

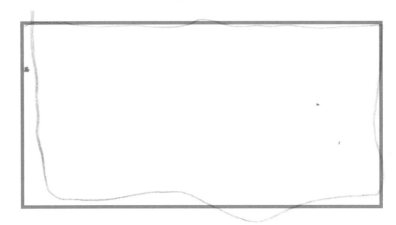

Trace each rectangle.

Did you know?
A rectangle and a square both have 4 sides.

Rectangle

These shapes are rectangles.

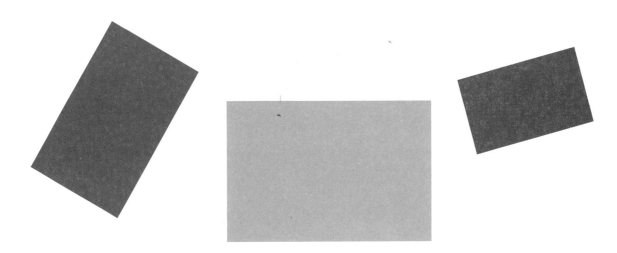

Circle each rectangle.

Hearts and Stars

red heart

yellow star

Color the hearts red. Color the stars yellow.

Groups and Patterns

Same and Different

Look at the first shape in each box.

Circle the shapes that are the **same**.

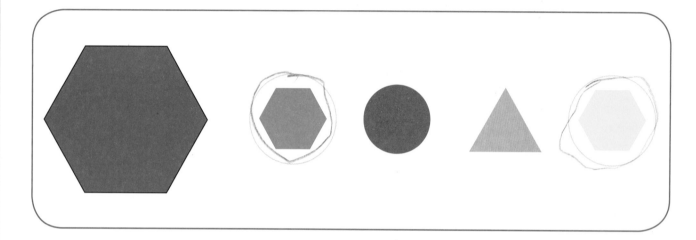

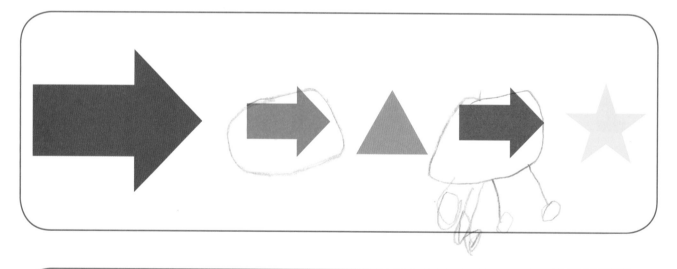

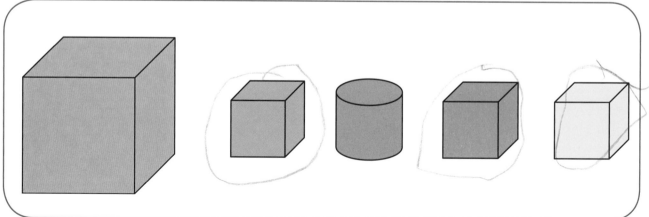

Same and Different

Look for things that are the same.

Draw lines to match them.

Same and Different

Look at the first shape in each box.

Color blue the shapes that are the same.

Color green the shapes that are different.

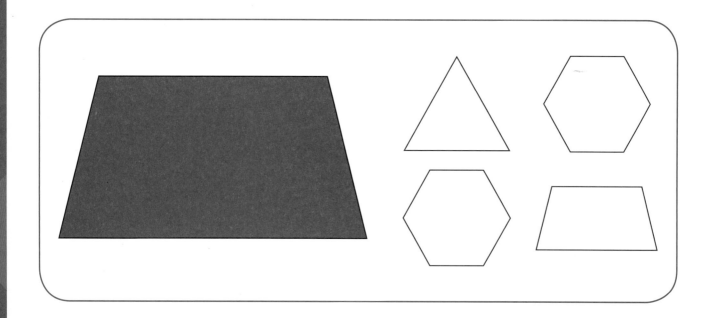

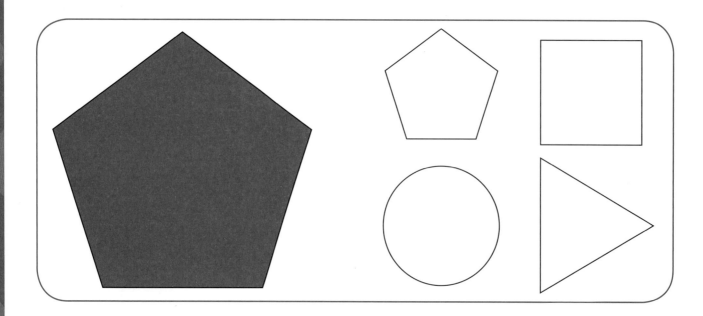

Same and Different

Look at the first picture in each box.

Draw an **X** on the pictures that are **different**.

Did you know?
Evergreen trees stay green all winter.

Groups

Look at the **group** in each box. Circle the thing that belongs to the same group.

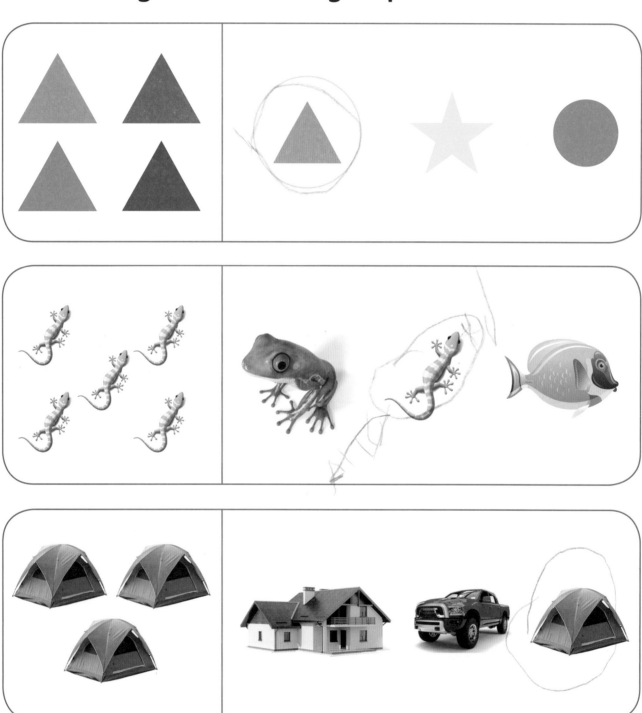

Did you know?
Gecko lizards are found in warm places all over the world.

Groups

Draw a line to match animals that belong to the same group.

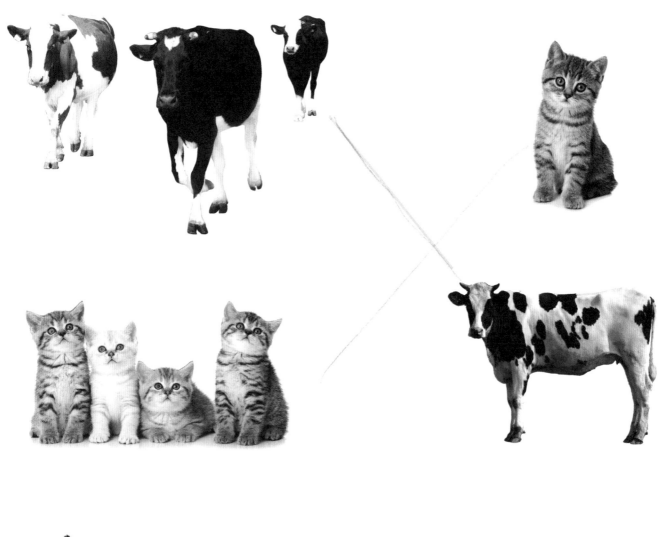

Long and Short

This pencil is long.

This pencil is short.

Circle the longer thing in each box.

Long and Short

Long and Short

In each box, color the **shorter** thing blue.

Color the **longer** thing red.

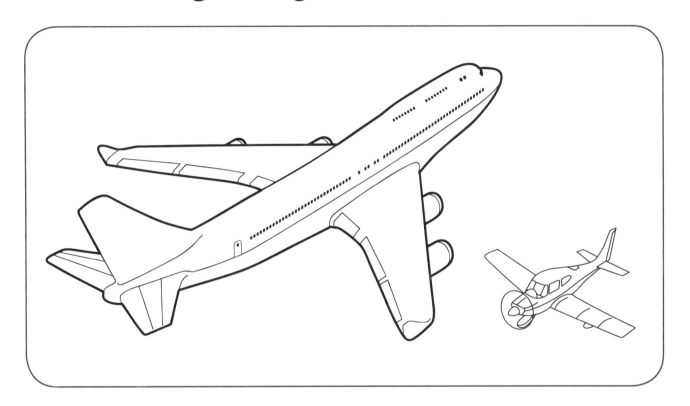

Short and Tall

This jar is **short**.

This jar is **tall**.

Circle the **shorter** thing in each box.

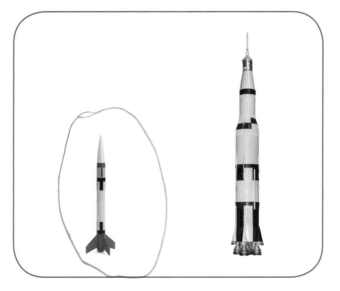

Did you know?
The violin and the bass violin are stringed instruments.

Short and Tall

Color the **taller** thing in each box.

Short and Tall

Heavy and Light

The elephant is heavy.

The mouse is light.

Circle the **heavier** thing in each box.

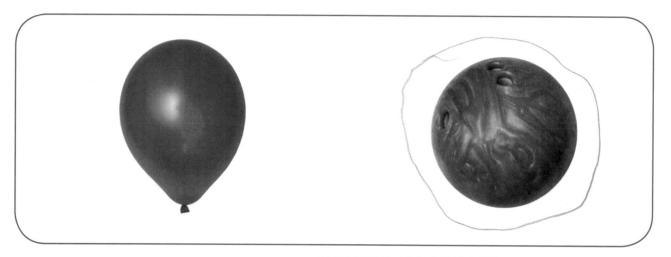

Did you know?
Elephants live in India and Africa.
They are the largest land mammal.

Heavy and Light

Color the **lighter** thing in each box.

Empty and Full

This glass is **full**.

This glass is **empty**.

Color the empty jug to make it full.

Empty and Full

Empty and Full

Circle the **empty** thing.

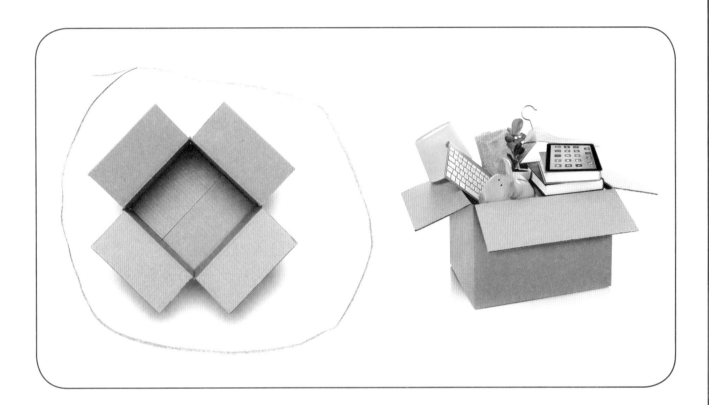

Empty and Full

More and Less

The small milk carton holds **less** milk than the big milk carton.

The big milk carton holds **more** milk than the small milk carton.

Circle the thing that holds **more** water.

More and Fewer

The car holds fewer people than the bus.

The bus holds more people than the car.

Circle the basket that holds fewer things.

Patterns

Look at the shapes in each pattern.
Circle the shape that comes next.

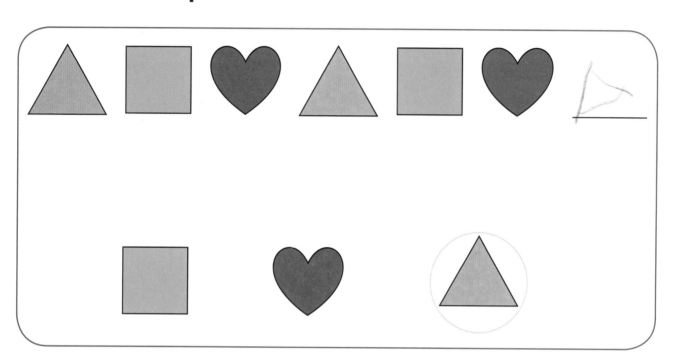

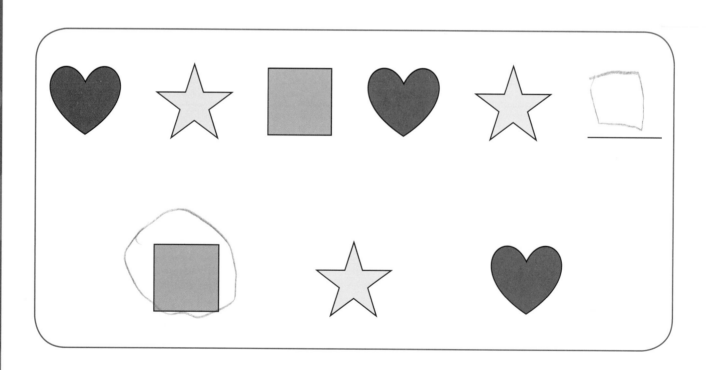

Patterns

Draw the next shape in each pattern.

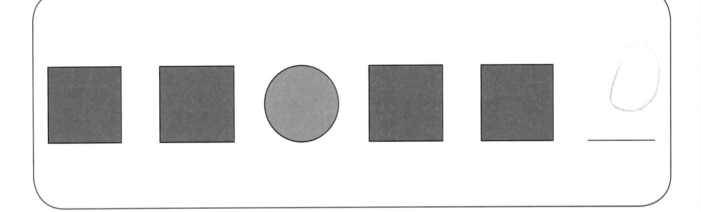

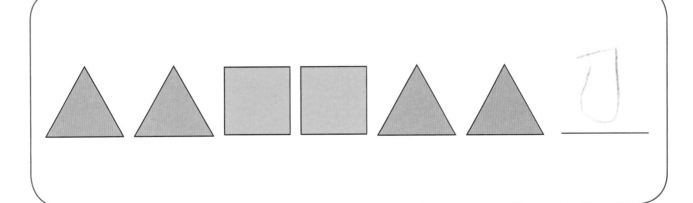

Patterns

Circle the next thing in each pattern.

Did you know?
Chimpanzees can live more than 27 years.

Numbers

Numbers 1 and 2

1 teddy bear

2 dolls

Count the toys. Circle the number.

1   (2)

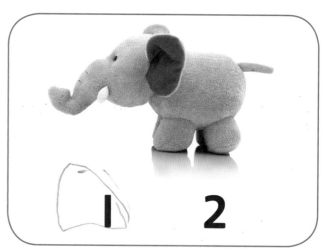

1   2

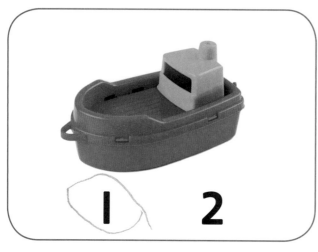

1   2

1   (2)

Numbers 1 and 2 ....

1 car

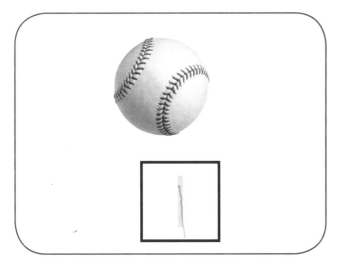

2 trucks

Count. Write the number.

1

2

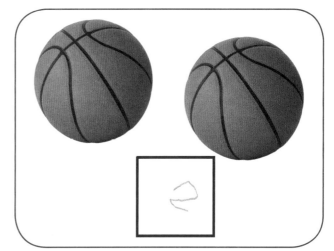

1

2

Numbers 3 and 4

3 stars

4 hearts

Count the shapes. Circle the number.

3   **4**

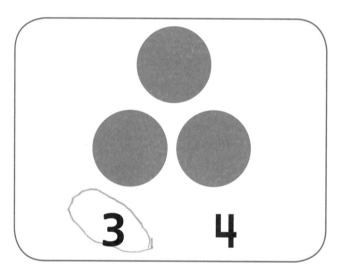

3   4

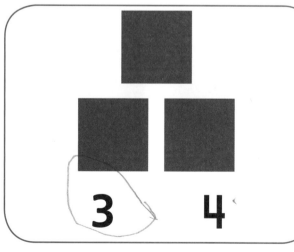

3   4

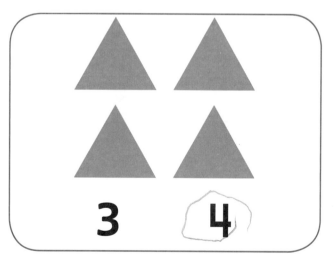

3   **4**

Numbers 3 and 4 ....

3 cats

4 dogs

Count the animals. Write the number.

4

3

4

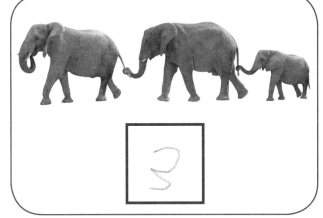

3

Did you know?
Grizzly bears sometimes eat salmon.

Numbers 5 and 6

5 circles

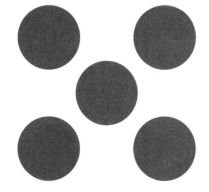

6 hearts

Count the shapes. Circle the number.

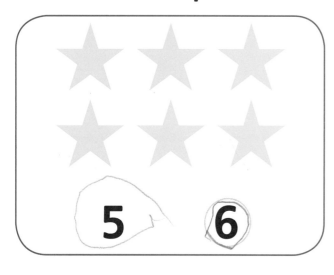

5   **6**

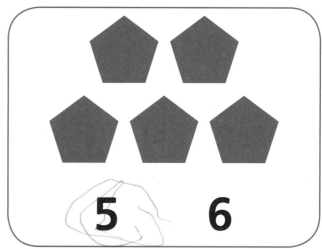

5   6

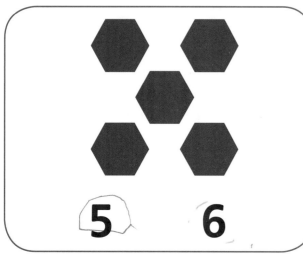

5   6

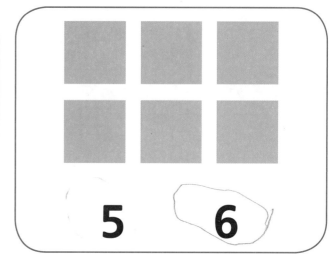

5   6

Numbers 5 and 6

5 chickens

6 eagles

Count the birds. Write the number.

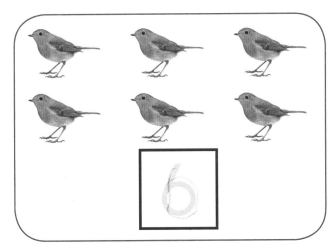

6

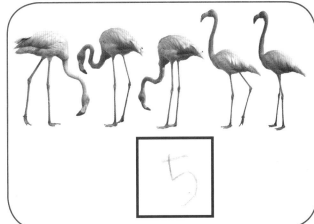

5

6

5

Did you know?
Flamingos can sleep standing on one foot.

Numbers 5 and 6

Numbers 7 and 8

7 roses

8 daisies

Count the flowers. Circle the number.

7 8

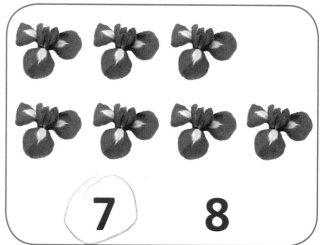

7 8

7 **8**

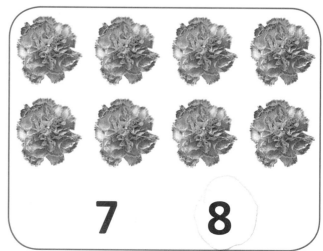

7 **8**

Numbers 7 and 8

7 airplanes

8 helicopters

Count. Write the number.

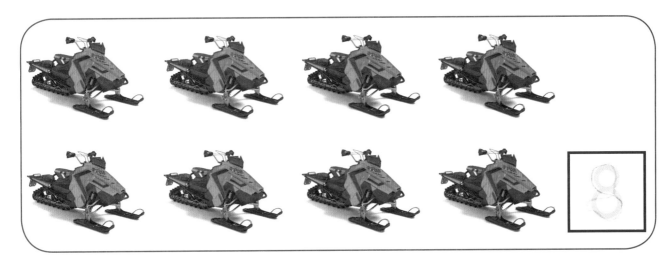

8

7

Did you know?
Riding a bicycle or tricycle is good exercise!

Numbers 9 and 10

9 triangles

10 squares

Count the shapes. Circle the number.

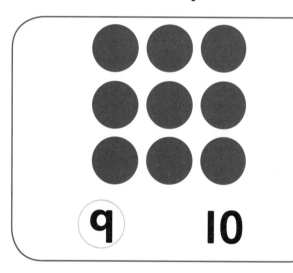

q   **10**

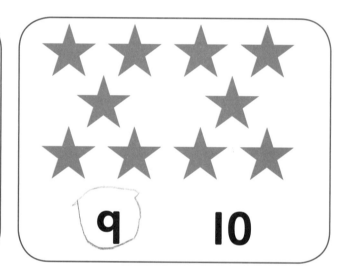

q   **10**

q   **10**

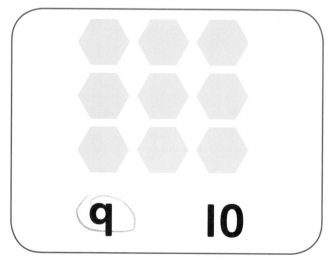

q   **10**

Numbers 9 and 10

9 bees

10 butterflies

Count the insects. Write the number.

10

4

Did you know?
Ants can lift up to 50 times the weight of their own bodies. That's like a child lifting a car!

Numbers 1 to 5

Count. Draw a line to the correct number.

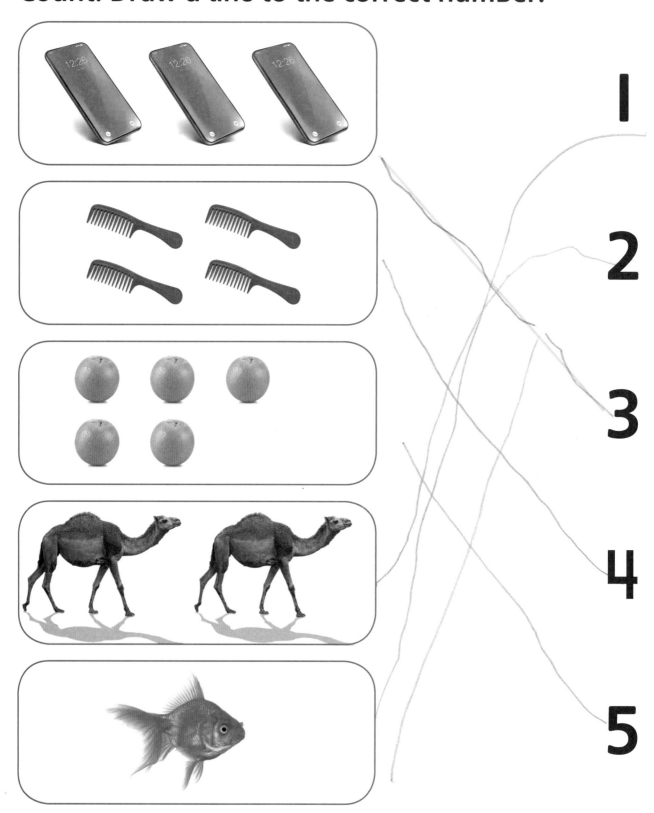

1

2

3

4

5

Numbers 6 to 10

Count. Draw a line to the correct number.

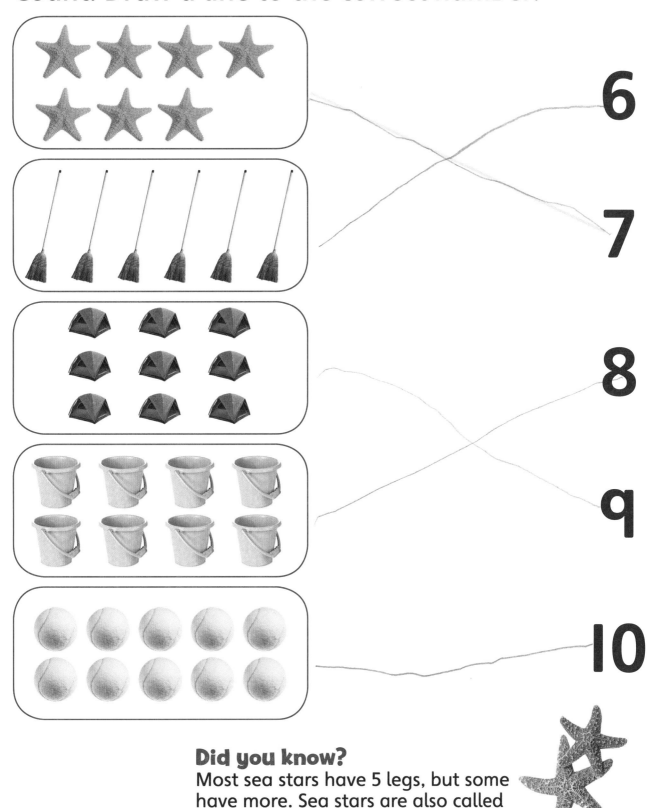

6

7

8

q

10

Did you know?
Most sea stars have 5 legs, but some have more. Sea stars are also called starfish, even though they are not fish!

Numbers 1 to 5 ....

Color the ducks to match the number.

1

2

3

4

5

Numbers 1 to 5 ....

Numbers 6 to 10

Color the dogs to match the number.

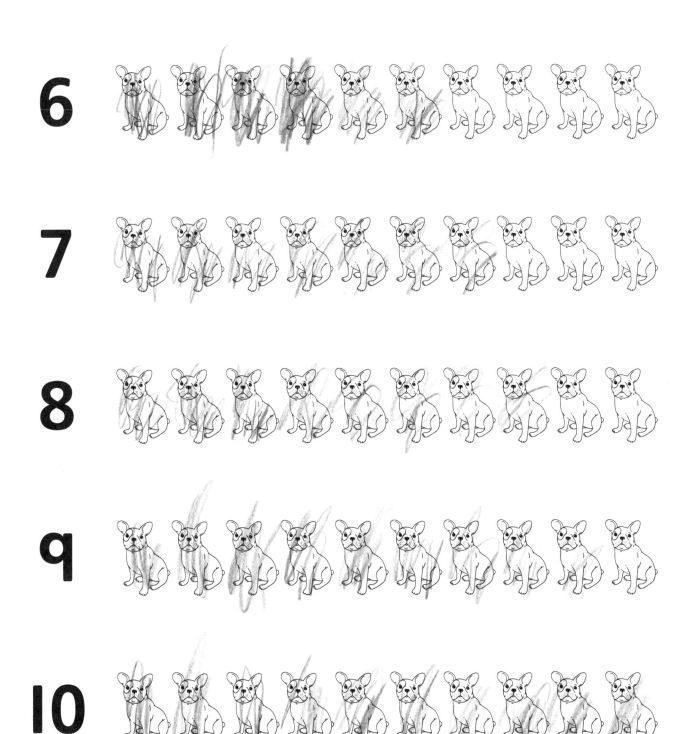

6

7

8

q

10

How Many?

Look at the picture. Count the chickens and the eggs. Circle the correct number for each.

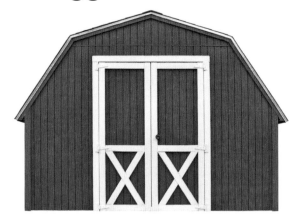

$\boxed{5}$ 6

2 $\boxed{3}$

How Many?

Look at the picture. Count the apples and the oranges. Circle the correct number for each.

 4 5

 5 6

Did you know?
Oranges and apples are full of important vitamins. Eating fruit can help you stay healthy.

Adding

Count to add. Write the correct number in the box.

 +  = 2

1   1

 + =

2   1

 +  = 4

1   3

Adding

Count to add. Write the correct number in the box.

2 + 3 = 5

3 + 3 = 6

3 + 4 = 7

Did you know?
In the fall, a maple leaf changes color from
green to red, yellow, or brown.

Adding

Count to add. Write the correct number in the box.

4

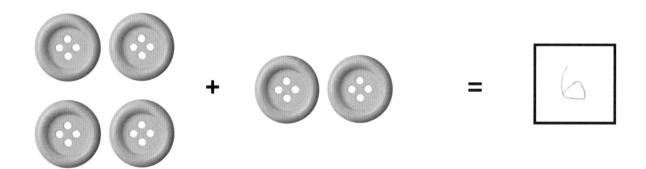

6

8

Comparing

Circle the group that has **more**.

Comparing

Circle the group that has **fewer**.

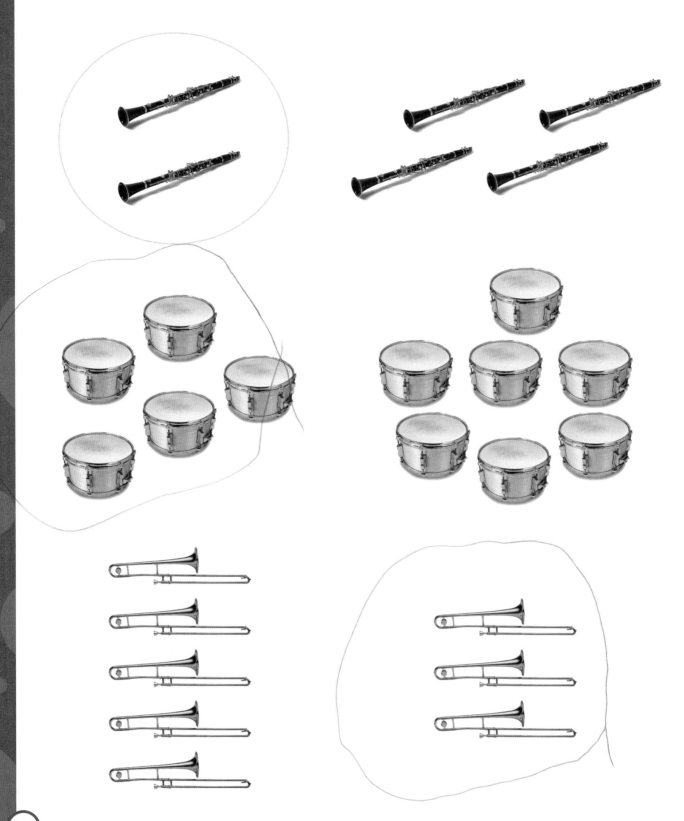

Social Studies

Everyone Has a Name!

Make your name with alphabet stickers.
Then write your name.

Everyone Has a Name!

Whose names do you know?

Write some on this page. You can use stickers to help!

Family

Mothers and fathers are **parents**.
Circle the parents in these pictures.

More Family!

Families come in many sizes.

People in families can be many ages.

Sometimes good friends are like family.

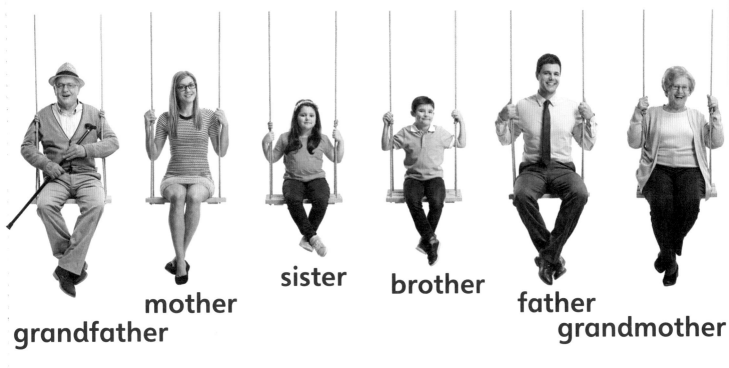

grandfather

mother

sister

brother

father

grandmother

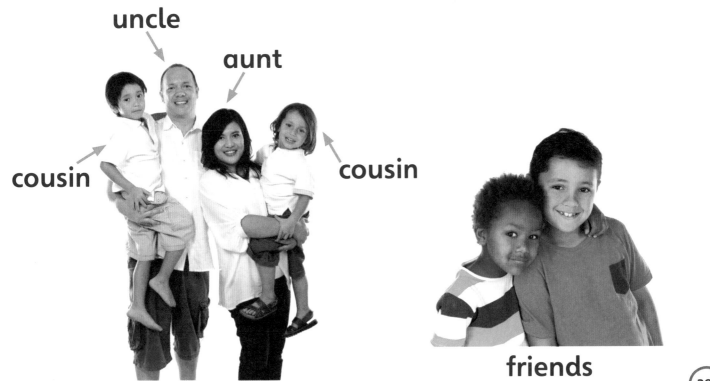

uncle

aunt

cousin

cousin

friends

Family and Friends

Think about family and friends who live with you or near you. Draw them here.

Did you know?
Many animals live in family groups. Aunts and other adult elephants may help take care of babies.

Eye Color

Eyes can be many colors.

What color are your eyes?

Circle the color that is closest to yours.

Draw a picture of your face. Color your eyes.

Brown Eyes

More people have brown eyes than any other color. Circle the brown eyes.

Hair Color

Hair can be many colors.

What color is your hair?

Circle the color that is most like yours.

Did you know?
Hair color can change when people get older. Some animals get gray hair too.

Signs

Signs help us when we drive, ride, or walk on streets.
Circle the signs that you have seen.

Circle the signs that tell you to **stop**.

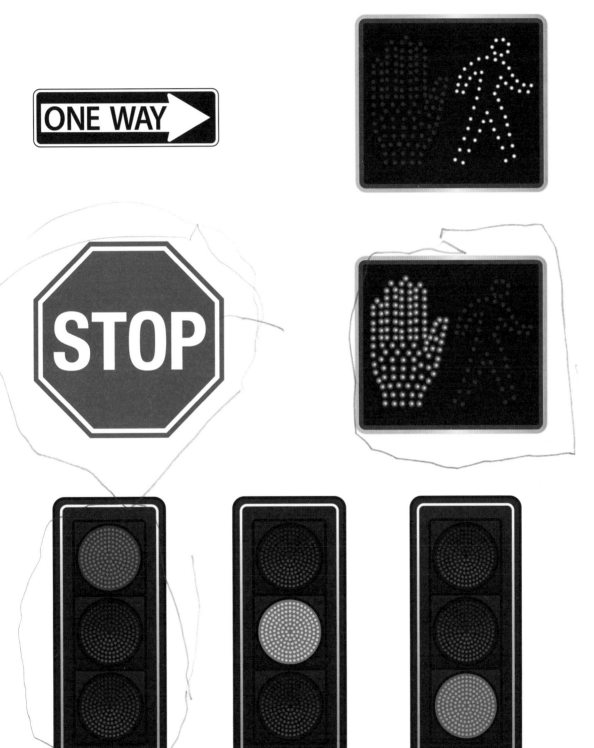

Address

A street address has a **number** and a **name**.

20 FIRST AVENUE

187 Main Street

What is your street address?

number   street name

Towns and States

Your address also has a town or city and a state.

Chicago is a city in the state of Illinois.

What is the name of your town or city?
What is the name of your state?

town or city

state

Homes

People live in many kinds of homes.

Have you seen homes that look like these?

Color the pictures.

Your Home

What does your home look like?

Draw a picture of your home.

Places

Draw a line to match each place with what happens there.

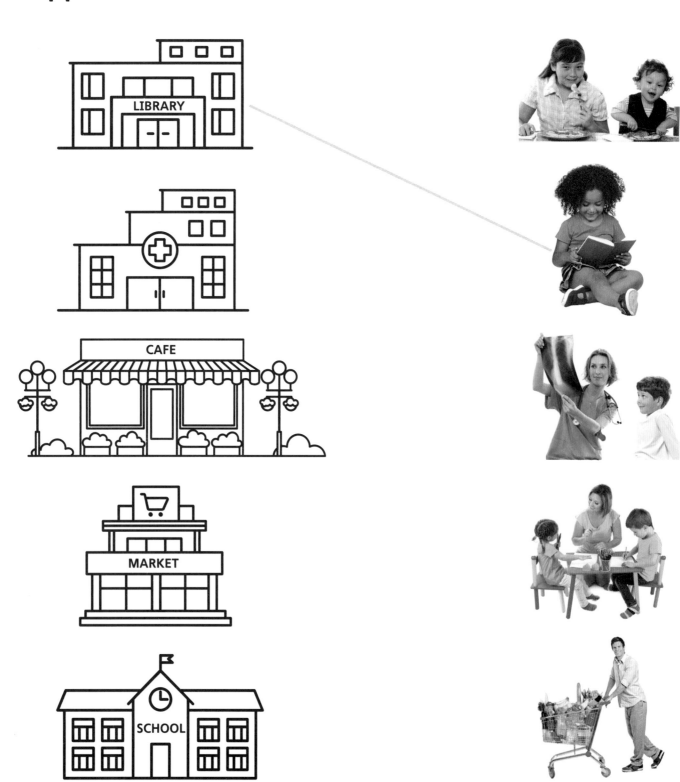

Rules

**Rules help us stay safe and get along with others.
Circle the pictures of rules you follow at home or
in school.**

Make your bed.

Wash your hands.

Raise your hand.

Put away toys.

Line up.

Be quiet.

Rules for Where? ....

Draw the place that has these rules.

Do not dive.

Do not run.

Do not eat or drink.

Use the ladder.

Wear a swimsuit.

Slippery – be careful.

Helping

We help each other at home.

We help each other at school.

Circle the things that you do to help.

Jobs

Talk about each person's job.

How does it help people or animals?

Do your parents have jobs?
Draw one of them at work.

More Jobs

Circle the jobs that you can name.

Your Job

Have you thought about a job that you would like to do someday? Draw yourself at work.

Travel

People can go places using vehicles.
Circle the vehicles that you have traveled in.

Here are more ways to go places.

Circle the ones that you have used.

Then draw yourself traveling in your favorite way.

Day and Night

Color the things you do in the day.
Circle the things you do at night.

Day and Night

Did you know?
Many animals sleep during the
day and are awake at night.
This is called being **nocturnal**.

Feeling Happy

Sometimes people feel **happy**. When people are happy, they might smile or laugh. Circle the pictures of children who look happy.

Feeling Sad

Sometimes people feel **sad**. When people are sad, they might frown or cry. Circle the pictures of children who look sad.

Feeling Sad

Feeling Angry

Sometimes people feel **angry**. When people are angry, they might frown or feel hot. Their faces or bodies might get tight.

When you are angry, you can do things to calm down. Circle the things that you have done or would like to do.

Take deep breaths.

Sit and relax.

Blow bubbles.

Talk about it.

Exercise.

Feelings

People can have many different feelings. Circle the ways that you have felt.

happy

surprised

tired

angry

scared

sad

My Feelings

What do you do to calm down if you are angry? Draw it here.

What makes you feel happy? Draw it here.

Science

Nature is all around us!

Plants and animals are parts of nature.

Circle plants and animals that you have seen.

flowers

butterfly

plant

bird

tree

cat   dog

Through the Window

Look out a window.

Draw plants or animals that you can see.

Big and Small

Look around the room.

Draw the biggest thing you see.

Draw the smallest thing you see.

Weather

Every day has **weather**.

Draw lines to match each small picture to the sky it goes with.

What's Your Weather?

Is it sunny today? Is it raining?

Draw your weather.

What's Your Weather?

How Does it Feel?

Circle the **scratchy** thing.

Write a **W** by the **wet** thing.

Draw a line under the **soft** thing.

Draw a box around the **sticky** thing.

Draw an **X** over the **hard** thing.

Animal Outsides

Match each animal to its outside.

Then color the animals.

duck

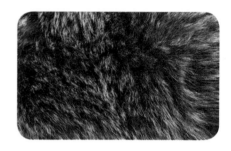

bear

fish

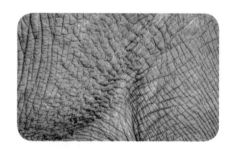

elephant

Tools and Tasks

Match each tool to what it is used for.

hammer

whisk

scissors

paintbrush

Fast and Slow

One side is **fast**. One side is **slow**.

Draw yourself on the fast side.

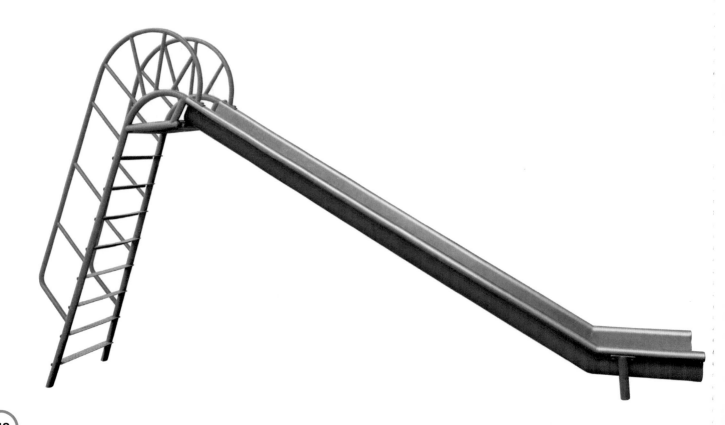

Ice and Steam

Ice is **cold**. Steam is **hot**.

But they are made of the same thing.

Circle what ice and steam are made of.

Light

A lightbulb is hot and bright.

Draw other things that give **light**.

How Do Plants Grow?

Read about how plants grow.

Look at the pictures.

We plant seeds in the soil.

A sprout comes out of the ground.

The stem grows.

Leaves grow.

leaves

sprout

seed

stem

Parts of a Plant

Color the picture.

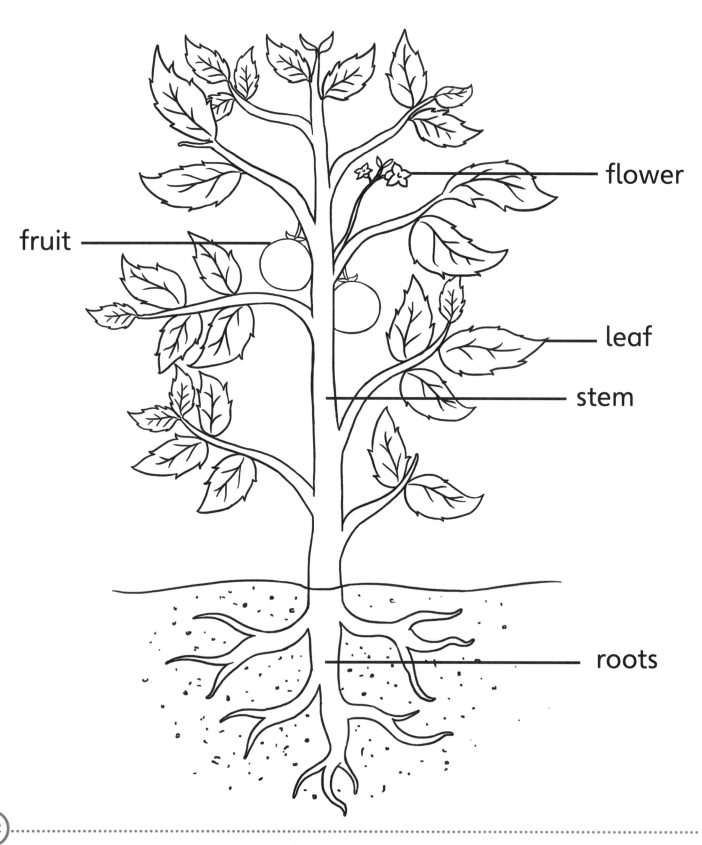

fruit

flower

leaf

stem

roots

Two Trees

Some trees have leaves. Other trees have needles.

Draw lines to match the parts to the trees.

Did you know?
Pinecones are full of tiny seeds. Some of the seeds will grow into new trees.

A Tree in Spring

! Trees have green leaves in spring.

Color the tree for spring.

A Tree in Fall

! Leaves turn different colors in the fall.

Color the tree for fall.

Animal Pairs

Draw lines to match the mother and baby animals.

Animal Homes

Color the animal that lives in each home.

Then color the home.

Animal Homes

Animal Foods

Match each animal to its food.

Animal Foods

More Animal Homes

**What animal would live in each of these homes?
Draw pictures to answer.**

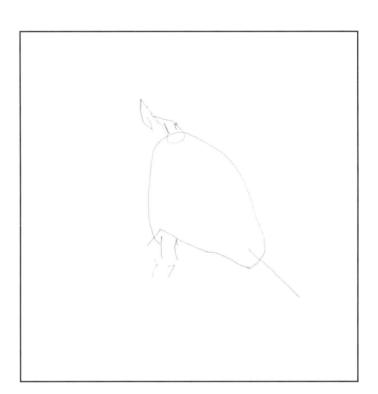

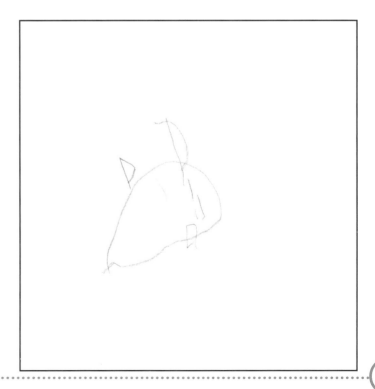

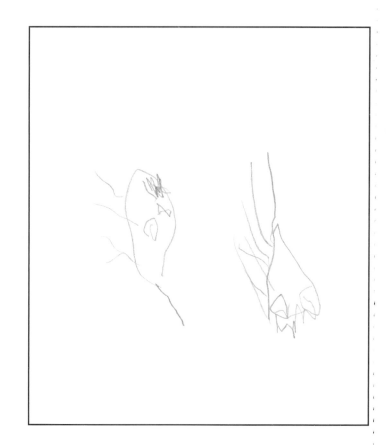

Senses

We have five **senses**. Look at the picture. The baby can **smell** with her **nose**. Say the parts of the baby for the other senses.

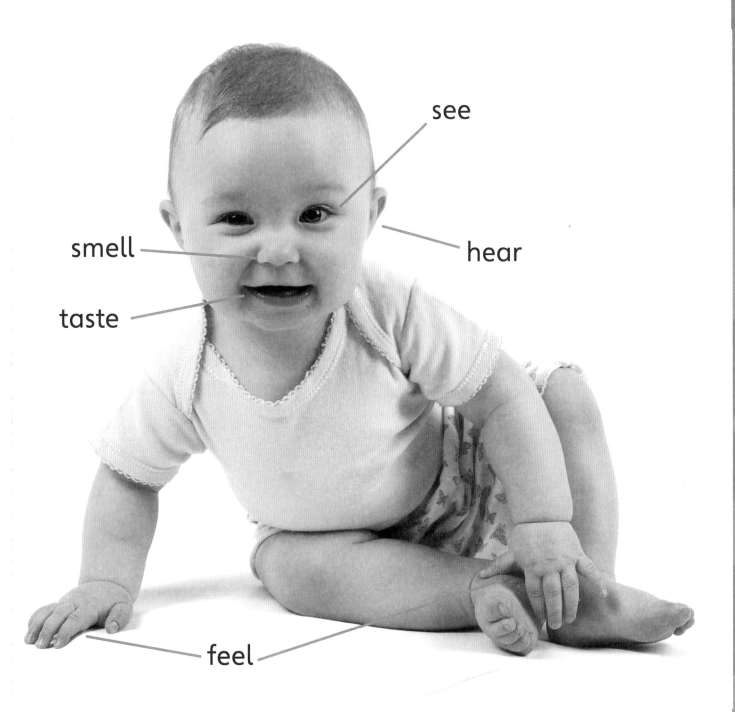

see

smell

hear

taste

feel

Using Your Senses

Circle the things you can **taste**.

Draw a line under the things you can **hear**.

Veggies Rule!

Circle each **vegetable**.

Fantastic Fruit

Circle each **fruit**.

Let's Keep Clean!

Circle the pictures that show how to get clean.

Let's Keep Clean!

Did you know?

Sing two verses of "Happy Birthday" while you wash your hands. When you're done singing, you have washed your hands long enough!

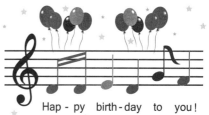

Hap - py birth - day to you !

Healthy Habits

Color the picture.

Healthy Habits

Hands-on

Now I know my ABCs!

A B C D E F

G H I J K L M

N O P Q R S T

U V W X Y Z

Cut out the letter cards on the next pages.

Use them to practice your letter sounds.

Then cut out the number cards.

Use them to practice counting.

A

B

C

X

Y

Z

Aa   Bb

Cc

Dd

Ee

Ff

Gg

Hh

Ii

Jj

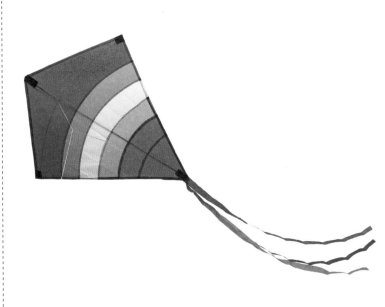

Kk

Ll

Mm

Nn

Oo

Pp

Qq

Rr

Ss

Tt

Uu

Vv

Ww

Xx

Zz

1
2
3
4
5

6
7
8
9
10

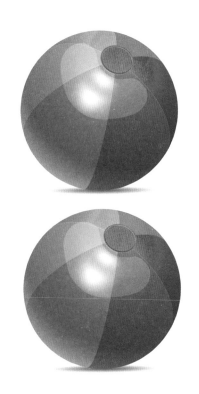

4 3

1 2

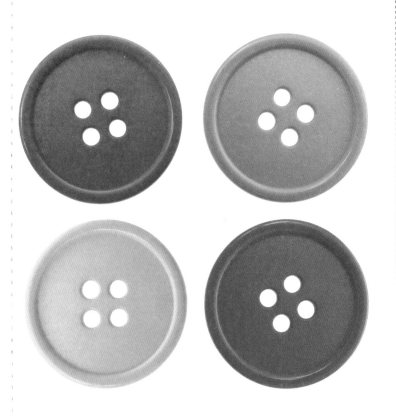

3

4

5

6

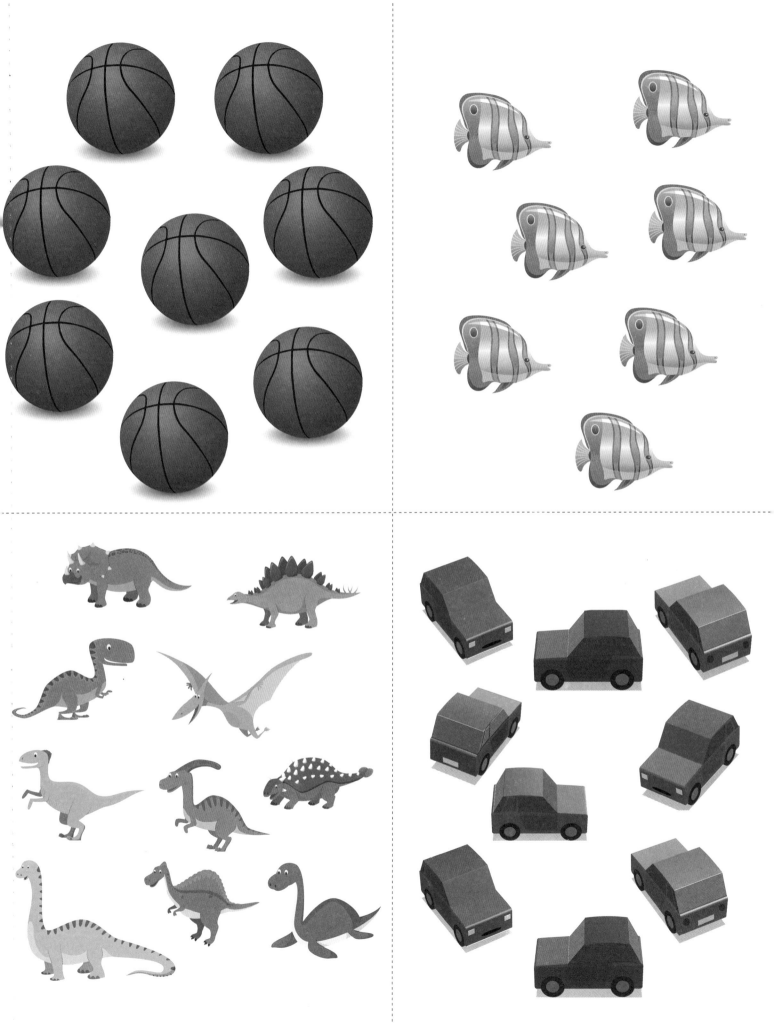

7

8

9

10

Coloring Shapes

Color the shapes. Use these colors.

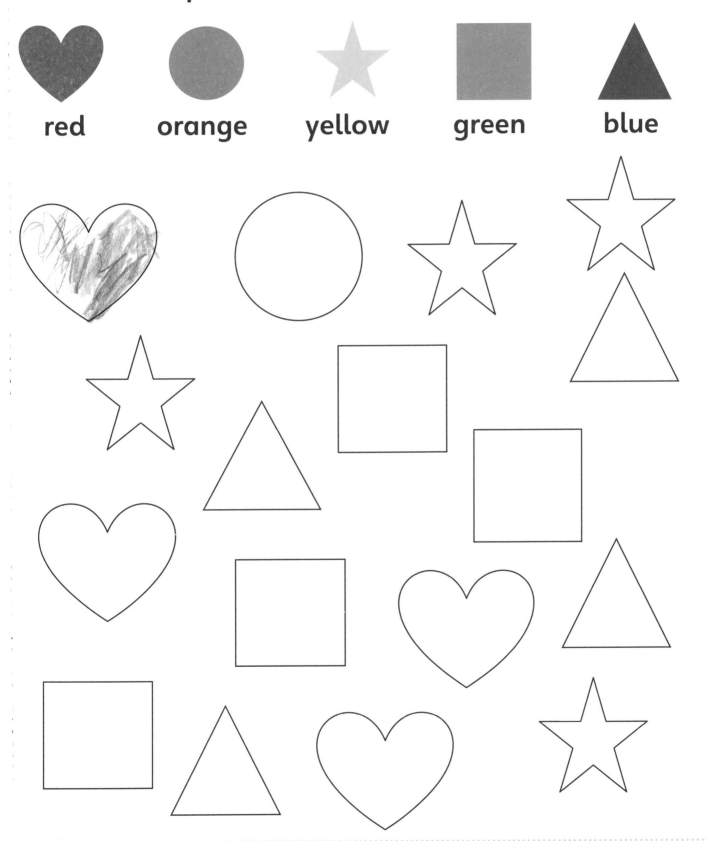

red   orange   yellow   green   blue

At the Park

Find and color the hidden pictures.
Then color the rest of the picture.

Hidden pictures: banana, heart,
watermelon, fish, spoon, ice cream

Color by Number

Color the picture. Use these colors.

1 yellow   2 red   3 purple   4 blue   5 green

Animals on the Farm

Count the animals on the farm.
Write the number of each kind of animal.

 2

 5

 1

 2

 2

 4

 3

Dot to Dot

Connect the dots from 1 to 10.

Start at 1 and go in counting order.

Color the picture.

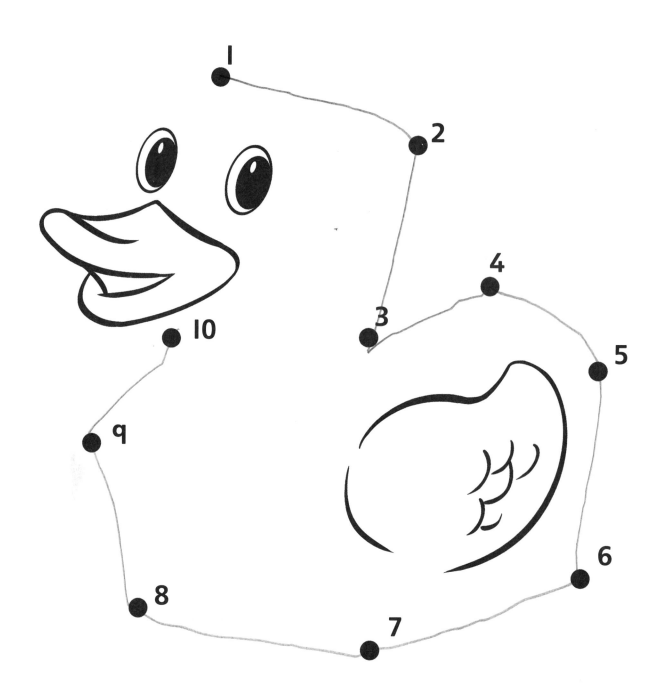

Brushing Order

Cut out the steps for brushing your teeth.
Glue them in order on the next page.

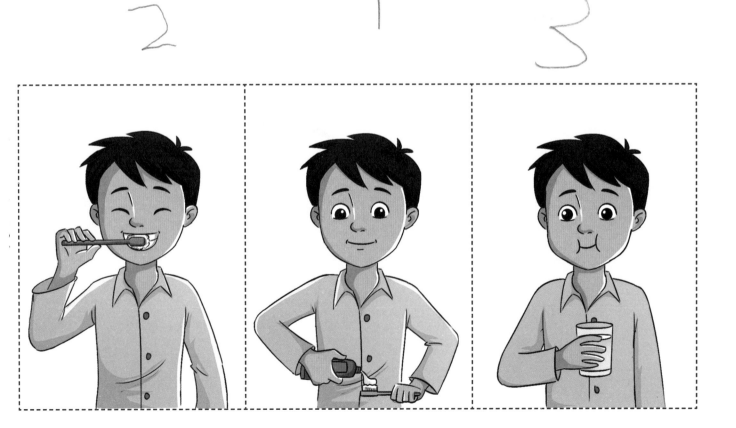

Step 1	Step 2	Step 3

Tangrams

Cut out each tangram piece.

Use them to make the pictures on the next pages.

You can use the pieces to make your own pictures.

Make sure not to glue them down.

Tangrams

Tangrams

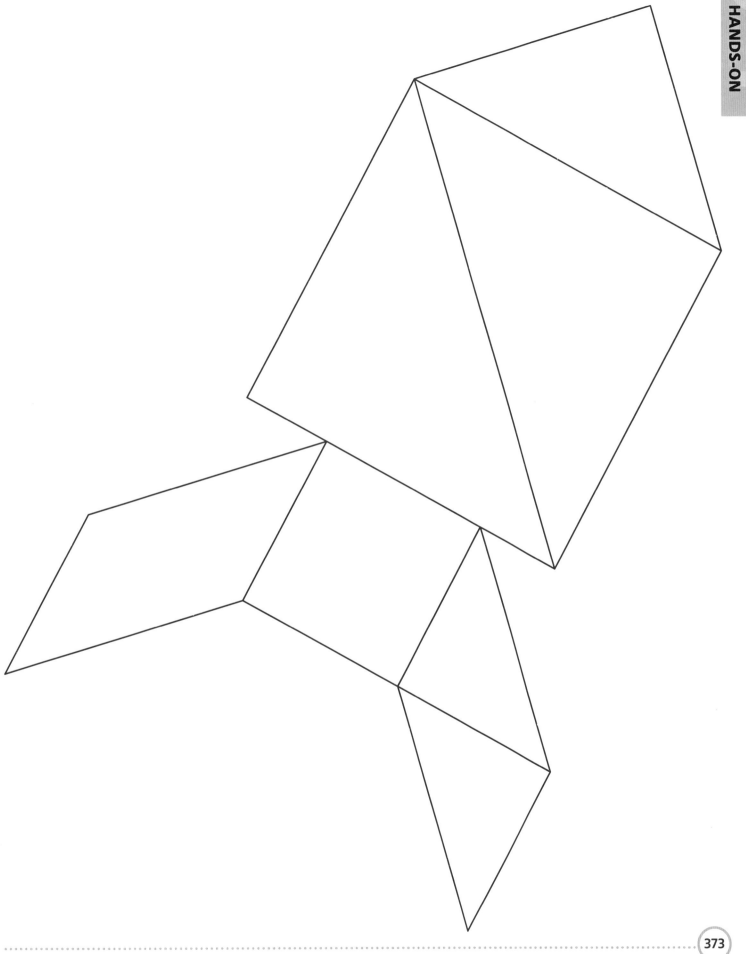

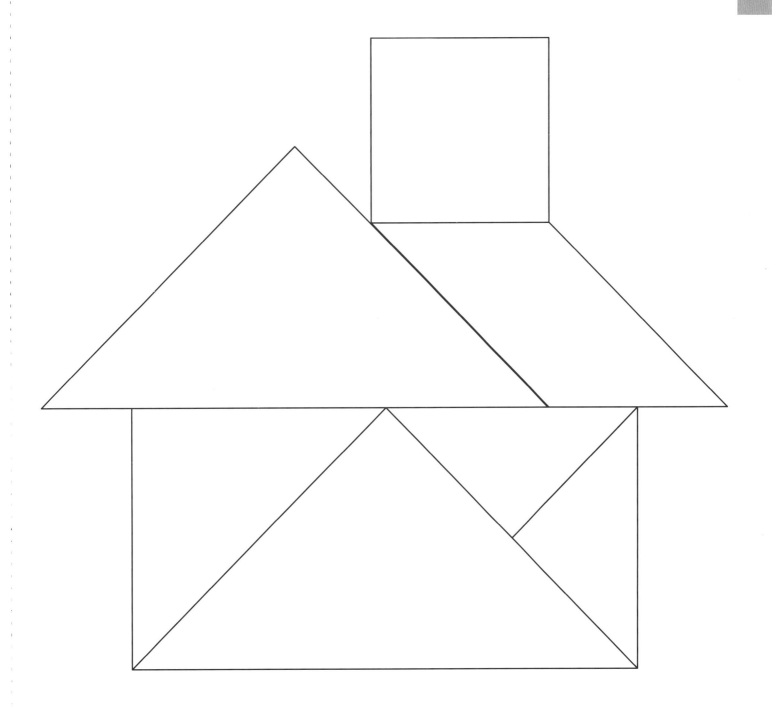

Glue each set of cookies onto a cookie sheet.

Mouse Maze

Help the mouse find the cheese.

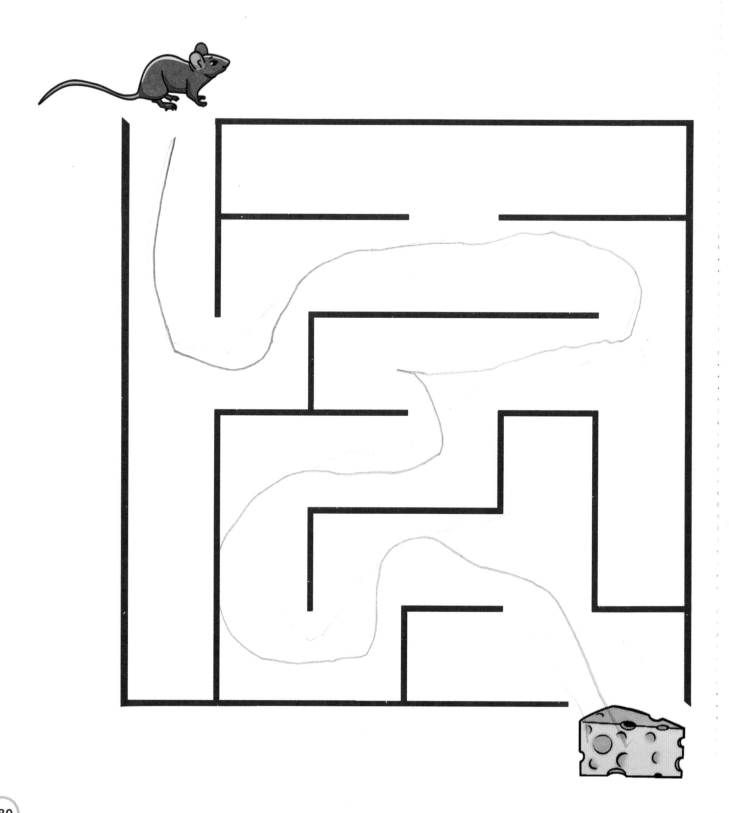

Color by Number

Color the picture. Use these colors.

1 green   **2** brown   **3** yellow   **4** blue

Recycling

Cut out the pictures. G̶ ̶ ̶ ̶ ̶ ̶ ̶ ̶ ̶ ̶ ̶e correct recycling bin̶

PLASTIC

PAPER

NEWS

WORLD

SCIENCE

BUSINESS

SPORT

GLASS

Giraffe Heights

Cut out the giraffes. Glue them in order.

shortest   tallest

Draw your own pictures with different heights!
Draw giraffes or another animal.

shortest   tallest

Dot to Dot

Connect the dots from I to I0.

Start at I and go in counting order.

Color the picture yellow or orange.

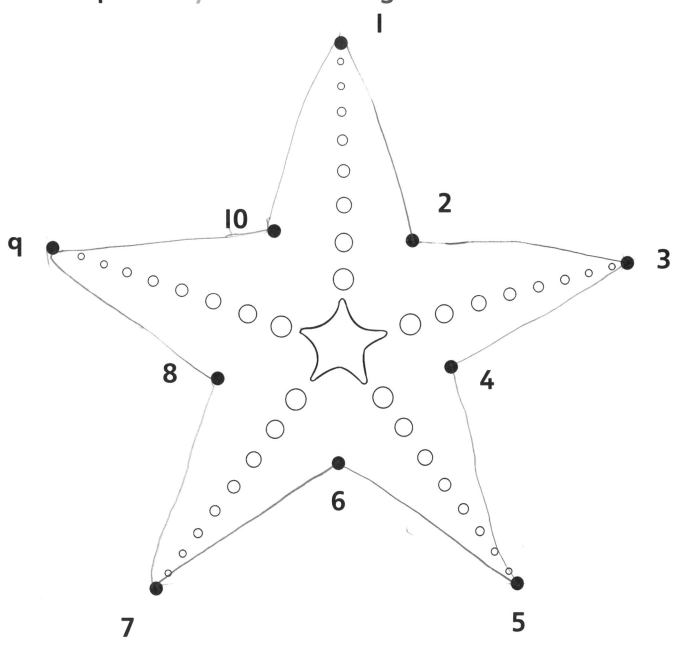

Same or Different

Circle the picture in each row that is **different**.

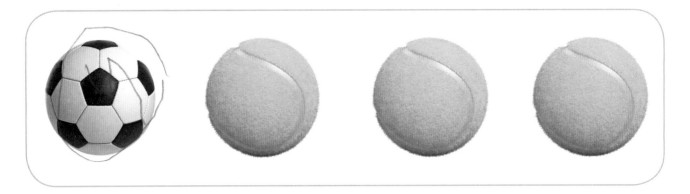

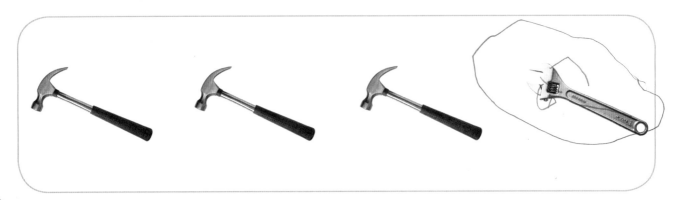

Healthy Eating

Color the healthy food.

Draw an X on the unhealthy food.

Coloring Shapes

Color the shapes. Use these colors.

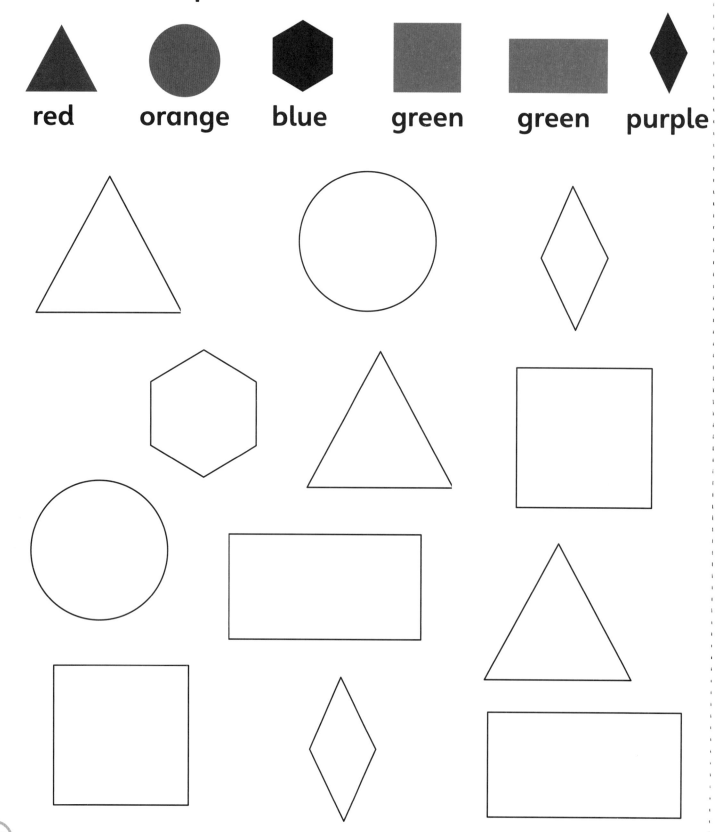

red   orange   blue   green   green   purple

Patterns

Draw the shape to finish each pattern.

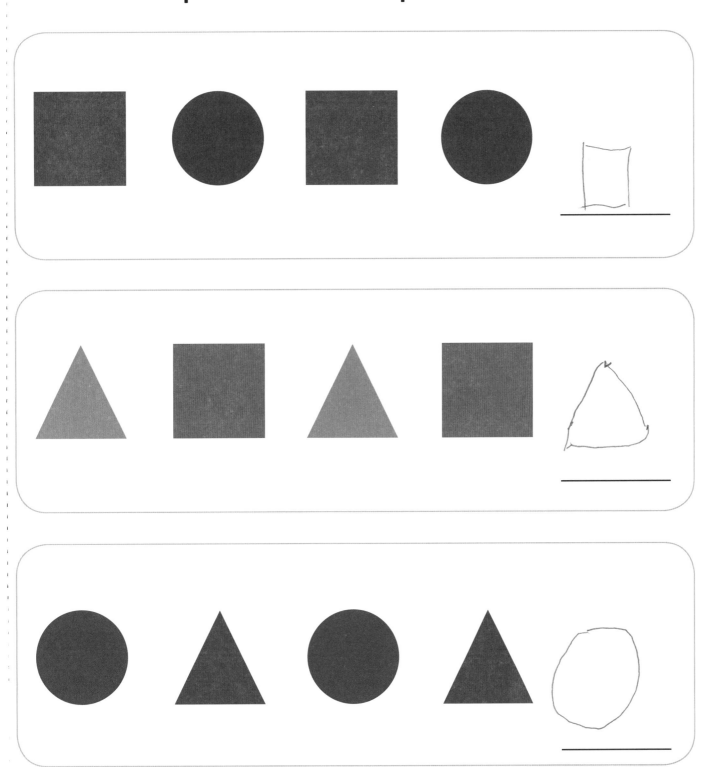

What Goes Together?

Draw lines to match pictures that go together.

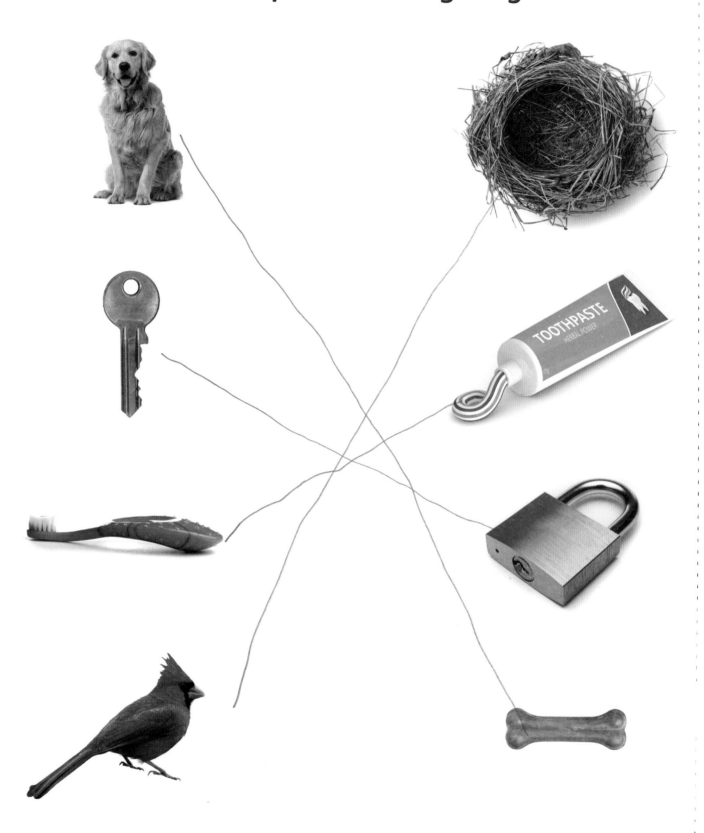

Hand Washing

We wash our hands to keep germs away and stay clean and healthy. Cut out the pictures. Then turn the page and glue them in the right order.

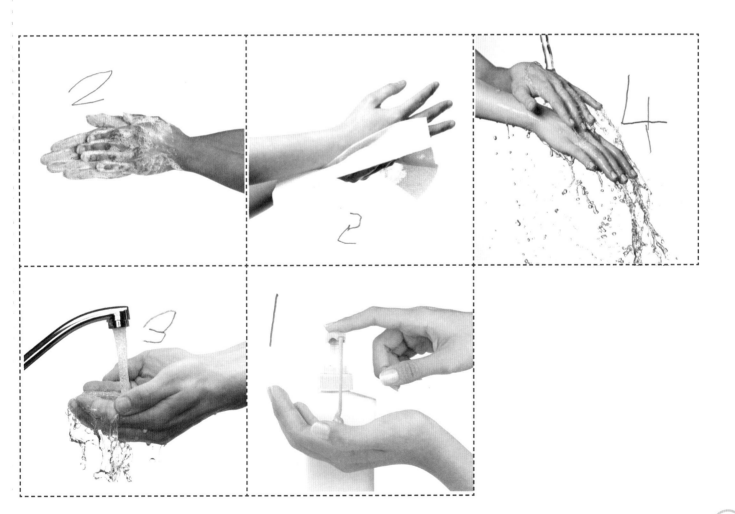

Circle the pictures of children who need to wash their hands.

Hand Washing

Glue the pictures to show the correct order.

First, get hands wet.

Next, get soap.

Next, scrub hands.

Then, rinse hands.

Last, dry hands.

Circle the pictures of children who should wash their hands to stay healthy.

A Book About Me

Draw your favorite thing to do.

I like to eat

Draw your favorite food.

My name is

VARUNTEE

Draw a picture of you!

I am ___3___
years old.

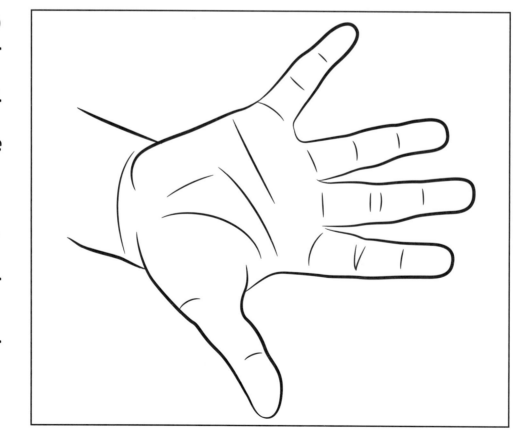

Color the fingers to show how many years old you are.

Wonders of Learning

Well done!

Pre-Kindergarten

WORKBOOK
COMPLETED

CERTIFICATE

Congratulations to:

....

(name)

for completing this **Wonders of Learning** workbook.

You are a learning star!

What was your favorite part of the book?

What do you want to learn about next?

....
(parent)

....
(date)

B C D

F H I I J

K K L L M M O O

P Q Q T

U W W X X Y

Z Z b b b

c c d d d

f f f g g g

i j j k l

l m m n

p

t

w